headwork c

Frankenstein

MARY SHELLEY
adapted by Michael Thomson

OXFORD
UNIVERSITY PRESS

1 ∾ LETTER FROM ROBERT WALTON TO HIS SISTER, MRS MARGARET SAVILLE

My dear sister,

The last time I wrote to you I was in St Petersburg*. The Russian winter was cold, but nothing can match the bitter cold of this ice. It is all around us and the ship is trapped. If we escape from the ice, I will post this letter when we return to St Petersburg. You will guess that I have reached the North Pole. You know that I always hoped to explore the frozen wastes* of the North. Well, soon after my last letter I had my chance. I was given command of a ship that was to explore the icy seas north of Russia. At last I could travel to a place that no other man had ever been to before.

We had not gone far when icebergs began to float by the ship like faithful dogs. The ship was made to be strong so that ice would not crush it. Yet it was frightening to see these huge lumps of ice sail by us. As we got near to the North Pole, something so strange happened that I can barely believe it myself. Let me tell you the story.

The ice had been getting thicker day by day. At last the ship could not move. We were stuck in a field of ice that spread as far as the eye could see. It was freezing cold and mist clung to the ship like smoke. One day, when the mist had cleared, we saw a black speck in the distance. Slowly it drew near. We saw that it was a man with a sledge. The dogs pulled the sledge and he moved along the ice at speed. He grew closer still and I gasped aloud. The man, if it was a man, seemed to be about eight feet tall. There was something odd about the way he moved and his face seemed lumpy somehow. I could not see clearly and the sledge soon disappeared into the distance.

What he was doing on these icy wastes, I did not know. Then, the next day a second strange thing happened. The wind began to blow and the ice began to break up. The look-out called, 'Man overboard*!' When we looked we saw a man lying on a small iceberg. He had not fallen overboard but had been carried towards us on his ice raft! Quickly we lowered a rope over to him and pulled him aboard*. He was frozen and seemed very ill. I had him taken down to my cabin. We wrapped him in blankets to warm him up. Then he was able to talk.

'Captain Walton, at your service,' I said.

'Victor Frankenstein,' he replied, rather faintly. 'Thank you for taking me aboard,' he went on. 'Perhaps it would have been better to let me sail on and die.'

'Nonsense, man!' I said. 'But how did you come to be in such a place?'

'I was on a sledge. Some of the dogs died of the cold. The rest of the dogs and the sledge fell into the water when the ice broke up.'

'But what were you doing here?' I asked.

'I have a task* to do.' He made as if to get up and go out into the ice again. Then he fell back onto my bed. 'I was seeking someone who was running from me,' he said, barely* able to talk.

'I think I may have seen him!' I cried. 'A huge man went by on a sledge like yours, only yesterday!'

At these words Frankenstein sat up. A spark of life came into his eyes and he shouted, 'It is him. That horrible creature!' Then, once again, the effort was too much for him and he sank back on the pillow.

Over the next few days I learnt to like the man. We talked about many things when he was able. Yet he seemed unhappy. He had bad dreams and did not sleep well. One day he said, 'You have been kind to me, Walton. You seem to be looking for the truth, like me. I must tell you the terrible secret that is burning inside me. It may serve as a warning to you and to mankind*. Soon I am going to die and I must ask something of you. Yet I cannot ask it until you hear the whole story.'

This, my dear Margaret, is what he had to say. I made notes as he spoke and this is his story.

2 ∾ VICTOR FRANKENSTEIN'S STORY: MY EARLY LIFE

I grew up in Switzerland in the city of Geneva. My father and mother were loving parents. Perhaps it was this love that kept me from going mad in later years. You will see why as my tale unfolds.

At first I was an only child. Then, one day, my parents visited a poor part of the city. In those days some places in the city were very poor. Many people had little money for food. Their houses were run down and sometimes had no clean water. My parents helped out where they could. They took food and clothes to the poor people. They often worked to help the poor. It was there that they found Elizabeth. She was a little girl with fair hair and blue eyes. Her parents had died and she was an orphan*. She was living with a large family. They were very poor and had five children of their own. They could not care for Elizabeth very well as they had so little money. My parents felt sorry for Elizabeth and her foster parents*. So Elizabeth came to live with us. Soon we all loved Elizabeth because she was gentle and kind. How I wish I could have had the same love and kindness for others that both my parents had and Elizabeth had. Perhaps I would have been a better person. But I must keep my story in the right order. Let me go on.

I had a friend called Henry Clerval. He, Elizabeth, and I played and learnt together. We had such happy times. That was when my interest in nature began. I liked to look at living things in ponds, trees, fields, or anywhere they lived. I also liked to study the world around me. I read as much as I could. I liked to read what the Greeks and Romans had said about life. Some of these writers talked about the 'Fountain of Youth'. This was a secret that they thought would let people live forever. I had dreams about finding this secret. I did not find the Fountain of Youth, but I learnt much of their wisdom. I hoped that in the future I would find the key to life.

One day my father made a kite. He had heard about the experiments to attract lightning. He wanted the lightning to strike the kite and travel to the ground. The power of lightning and electrical forces were a wonder to me. I saw a lightning bolt strike an oak tree. The huge tree was burnt to a stump in one blast! If only I could use this power! Later I was to use this force to create* rather than destroy.

My childhood ended when my mother died. I was only seventeen years old. By now I had two brothers, Ernest and William. William was hardly more than a baby when our mother became ill. I sat by her as she died.

'Promise me,' she said in her soft voice, 'promise me you will marry Elizabeth. You are both made for each other.'

'I promise, mother,' I replied with tears in my eyes.

'And you, Elizabeth,' my mother said, 'look after the family and take my place when I am gone.'

We both made our promises and my mother died with a smile on her face.

From that day, things in my life began to change. I spent some time teaching my brothers, Ernest and William. Both were bright and I loved teaching them. William was very dear to us all as the youngest of the family.

At last I had to leave home and go to university*. I still wanted to find out about the world. There I would be able to learn much more. I left Elizabeth and Henry behind and I went far away to study. I was still young but the university was very keen to have me. I suppose I was a kind of genius. How I laugh at that now!

I worked hard. Chemistry* was my first love. The forces of life were my concern. The ebb and flow* of life was my world for two long years. I worked with a man called Professor* Waldeman. He helped me understand many things and I soon began to work all the time. I learnt as much as I could from the Professor and his friends. I hardly ever wrote home. I was driven* to find out about the world around me and there was no room for anything else in my life.

Soon I knew more than my teachers. Some of them did not like this and they mocked* my work. Others gave me hope that I was on the right track. Once I overheard two of my teachers talking.

Professor Kempe said, 'This Frankenstein has wasted his time. The Greek and Roman writings tell him nothing!'

'I disagree!' said Professor Waldeman. 'They had many ideas which we use now. They understood the way life forces worked.'

'Nonsense!' Kempe went on, 'all they talk about is making lead into gold.'

'You have not understood their texts*,' Waldeman said. 'Much of modern Chemistry is based on them. Still, I shall not argue with you. All I know is that I have gained a student who has overtaken me. Frankenstein will take what he needs from us and learn more!'

I did not make myself known to them but slipped away quietly. Both men were wrong, I said to myself. I meant to make the secret of life mine. Oh, I was so proud of myself then. I felt I could do anything and did not think that I might be making a mistake.

Biology* was the next stage in my studies. I studied the human frame*. I looked at how the body worked. To find out the secret of life, I started with death. I spent night after night where the dead had been laid out. I saw how men and women decayed*. I saw how the spark of life went out and how our brains, which we humans are so proud of, soon rotted. I dug up bodies from their graves. Late at night I could be found in churchyards. I did not fear the dark. What I feared was death. I saw how bodies, once beautiful and strong, became food for worms. I cut up the dead. I studied life and death. It was a kind of madness that came over me. I worked day and night. Then, at last, I had the secret. I knew how to create life!

3 ∾ I CREATE A CREATURE

I can see you looking at me with wonder, Walton. Yes, I did find the secret of life. I found out how to breathe life into the dead, but I shall not tell you. The secret shall go with me to my grave. You will see, as you listen to my story, that no one should know such things. The power to change nature should not be given to any person. But I am straying* from my story. Let me go on.

I had been given my own work space by the university. You see, they thought my work was important. Yet they did not understand it at all. I had a bedroom above the work room. I slept and ate in this room. I worked like this for nearly a year.

I had now found how to create a life force. Next I had to make a human being. I would make a large being. This would

make my work easier and I wanted my being to be better than a normal human. Once again, I went to the graveyards and hospital slabs[*]. I cut up arms and legs. I pulled out organs[*] from bodies. Liver, heart, kidney, these were all things I needed. I put bits of bodies together. I worked day and night. My face was pale and I hardly ate. It was filthy work with blood and gore everywhere.

I had no time for anything else. Many letters came from my father, but I did not write back. I slept badly. Then I began to sleep in the work room. It was as if I had a fever as I tossed and turned at night in my bed. At last, I was ready. I had made a man eight feet tall. He was huge and strong looking. But he had no life as yet. Giving him life was my final task – a task that would make me like a god! I looked down at him. I nearly gave up then. How dare I meddle[*] with life, I thought. I am not a god. But then my pride in what I could do took over. No! I would not destroy my work before I had finished. I would go on! I would show the world that I, Frankenstein, could do what no one had done before.

It was on a dark and rainy night in November that I finished my work. I had been waiting for an electrical storm. At last it came. Lightning crashed and thundered. Flashes of forked lightning lit up the roof of my house. I had placed a metal rod to catch the lightning. Here the electrical force of life would travel down into the room. I could then put the spark of life into the body laid out on the slab.

The rain streamed down my window panes. By the light of the candles I could see the body as it lay on the work table. It was pale and lifeless. The lines of stitches where I had sewn the body stood out in black. At one o'clock in the morning the final flash of power played over the body. A blue and yellow glow lit up the

room. The body bent like a bow as the lightning struck. Then it was still again. All was dark apart from the candle. Nothing happened at first. Had I failed? What had gone wrong?

Suddenly, the body twitched. I felt my heart beat madly as one eye opened. A dull yellow eye peered out at me. I looked at my creation*. He had well-shaped limbs. His hair was black and shining. The creature had fine white teeth. Was he trying to smile at me? I did not know. Perhaps if I had tried to talk to him then, things might have been different.

I looked at the rest of him. What would he be like? I could see that his body was not fine like his hair and teeth. I could see the flesh and blood vessels* showing beneath his dirty yellow skin. He had black lips and sunken eyes.

The creature lay there, breathing but not moving. I felt a feeling of disgust come over me. I should have been proud and happy, yet the creature seemed like a monster to me. I had hoped to be a god and yet I seemed to have made a devil. Unable to bear these feelings, I ran upstairs. I know I should have stayed but I was so tired. I fell onto my bed and into a deep sleep.

I dreamt a very bad dream. In my dream I saw Elizabeth. She was beautiful. I went up to kiss her. As my lips touched hers, she changed. Worms crawled in her eyes. Cobwebs fell around her face. I held a corpse* in my arms!

I woke in a cold sweat. The storm had stopped. In the dim light of the moon I saw the being I had created. The monster stood looking down at me. He looked human, but something was wrong. He was ugly and made me gasp in horror. It made me sick just to look at him. He opened his mouth. Was he trying to say something? No sound came from his mouth. All I could see were the white teeth and black tongue. The creature held out its hand as if to touch me. The horror of that face made me run downstairs.

I spent the rest of the night pacing about. I did not think what the creature was doing. Again, if I had thought more about the creature, things might have turned out for the better. But all I could think about was myself and what I had done. I had tried to make a new life. Yet it had not worked out as I had hoped. First of all, the creature was ugly. Second, the creature did not talk. I should have known this. It was like a baby in many ways. Yet at least it could walk! All night I went over and over what I had done.

Then, at dawn, there was a knock at the door. It was my friend, Henry Clerval, who had also come to the university to study. 'Henry!' I gasped.

He looked at me and said, 'My dear Victor. We were right to be worried for you. How pale and ill you seem!'

'I have been working all night,' I said. I could not bear to tell Henry what I had done. Leaving Henry, I ran up to the room. I went to check on the monster. I threw open the door. To my delight, the room was empty. The monster had gone!

4 ∾ WILLIAM DIES

My feelings about the monster were mixed. I was pleased that it had gone. I did not want to have anything to do with it. But I knew the creature was out there. What was it doing and how would it live? In some ways I was like a father with a bad child. I wanted to help, yet was glad that it was not there. Now that the monster had gone, I tried to forget what I had done. I had hoped to create a life. Instead, I had made a horrible monster.

It helped having Henry there. I felt that his turning up at that time was a sign to me. Of course it was just luck. All my family had thought I was ill. They had not heard from me. They sent Henry round to find out how I was. The next few weeks were like a bad dream. Henry thought I was ill as I seemed so strange to him. I did not tell him my secret. I should have tried to find the monster, but I wanted to forget him. I did not want to face up to my failure to make something good. I thought it was evil. Well, Walton, you will judge later if the creature was evil or not.

A letter came from my Elizabeth. She told me all the news from home. My brother, Ernest, now sixteen, wanted to join the army. She told me about my other brother, William. She said he was a sweet boy with blue eyes, rosy cheeks, and dark curly hair. She also told me about a new member of the household. This was a young woman called Justine. Elizabeth said she was kind and pretty. She was helping to look after William. If only I had known then how my actions would affect all these people.

Elizabeth's letter helped me return to the real world. Henry stayed with me that summer. It was a summer of fun. Henry was a good friend and helped me enjoy life again. I went back to university. I found I no longer wanted to study those dark secrets of life. I felt normal. Then the letter came from my father and my world was shattered. I can remember the letter almost word for word.

My dear Victor,

You have been waiting for this letter to fix the time of your return to us. How I wish things were that simple. I can't let you return without the dreadful news. Something awful has happened - William is dead! This is what happened.

Last Thursday we were all out walking. Ernest and William went on ahead. William went off to play. At first we did not worry, then Ernest went to look for him. He could not be found. It seemed that he was lost. I looked for him all night. Then, at 5.00 am, I found him. He lay still on the ground. Around his neck were the black and blue marks of fingers. He had been strangled! Our lovely boy, William, had been murdered.

When Elizabeth saw the body, she fainted. When she woke, she wept and cried, 'I lent William my locket*. He wore it around his neck. Now it has gone. The murderer took it!' She now blames herself. She says if she had not given William the locket, it would not have been stolen and he would still be alive. Please come home and comfort her, as well as your father.

I showed Henry the letter. We both wept and I shouted in rage, 'Who would murder a young child?'

'We must go back home, Victor,' Henry said. 'We must help your family.' We hurried to Geneva.

Before going to my family, I went to the park where they had

16

been walking. I made my way to the place where I had been told
William's body had been found. The sun was just going down
and it was dark and murky*. A storm had started and the rain
began to fall. The lightning flashed on the lake, which lit up like
a sea of fire. My tears joined the rain falling down my cheeks.
Then the lightning ripped through the sky again and I saw a
massive figure standing there. At once I saw that it was the vile
creature I had created. The horror of its face and size! The
creature had lifted its huge hands up to the sky. Then, somehow,
I knew. He had killed William! Some feeling deep inside me told
me. The perfect life I had hoped to create had become evil. I just
knew the monster was the murderer.

The creature turned to look at me. He seemed to know who

I was. A look of pain and sorrow came over his face. Then he turned and moved away. I ran towards him. Another lightning flash showed him climbing the cliffs by the lake. The creature's speed and strength were amazing. I ran after him but I could not keep up. Soon he had disappeared into the mountains.

I returned home. I knew who the killer was, but who would believe me? Should I go to the police? They would need more evidence* than my feeling that the monster had killed William. Also, who would believe that I had created such a thing? They would want to know why I had not said anything about it before. They would wonder why I had not told the university of my work and my creation. They would want to know why I had let the monster go. They would think me a madman. So, my dear Walton, see how our silence can start a chain of terrible events. The truth should be told at once. I should have taken more care of my creation. Now you will see how my story unfolds into more horror.

As I have said, no one would have believed that I had created such a monster. Even if they had, I found out that events had overtaken me[*]. Someone else was blamed and the police were certain they had found the killer.

When I returned home, I found Ernest and Elizabeth weeping. My father said, 'The murderer has been found out.'

'How could that be?' I cried. 'He cannot be found in the mountains.' Even then I thought that they must mean the monster.

'What are you talking about?' my father said. 'The mountains?'

I was silent. No one else had seen the creature. My father looked at me strangely. Then he went on, 'Yes, we have found the

murderer. The evidence is all there. Who would have thought that Justine, who seemed gentle and kind, could be so evil?'

'Justine! But…'

'Yes,' my father went on, 'when Justine's clothes were taken to be washed, Elizabeth's locket was found in her pocket. When the housekeeper* showed me the locket, I took it to the police. Justine herself seems very confused. She has been arrested.'

'But she is innocent,' I said. 'I am sure of it.'

'Well, we shall see,' my father replied. 'There will be a trial* and we will hear all the evidence.'

I did not say anything then. I felt sure that they would find Justine innocent and they would let her go.

The next day we all went to the courtroom*. Justine seemed calm. Yet as the trial went on, things did not go well. Justine had been out that night. She had been seen near the spot where William's body was found. She was seen near the same place the next morning too. She had seemed confused. When Justine was shown the locket, she had screamed and was taken to her bed. She had stayed there, pale and silent, until the arrest.

In the courtroom the lawyer* took out that same locket.

'Is this the locket?' he asked.

'Yes,' replied Justine quietly.

'How did it get into your pocket?'

'I don't know.'

'Whose is the locket?' the lawyer went on.

'It is Elizabeth's. I put it on William myself before he went for the walk.'

'Where did you go that night?'

'I went to visit my aunt. On the way back I heard that William had gone missing. I went out to search for him.'

'How was it,' the lawyer said, 'that you were so near where he was found dead and yet you did not see him?'

'I do not know,' Justine said, her head hung low. 'How I wish I had found him!'

'And,' the lawyer went on, 'what were you doing there the next morning? Why did you now have the locket which you say was William's?'

'I fell asleep in a barn*,' Justine said. 'I do not know how the locket came to be on me.' She began to cry and the lawyer sat down, looking pleased with himself.

Then Elizabeth spoke up for Justine to say how gentle and kind she was.

'Justine would never do such a thing,' Elizabeth said. 'She loved William like a brother. She was looking for him that night, just as we all were.'

I was grateful to Elizabeth. I knew Justine was innocent. Now she would not be found guilty, I was sure.

The next day I was sickened to hear that Justine had been found guilty. They would hang her that day! Elizabeth and I rushed to see her in prison. I would have to say something to the judge. Justine must not be hanged for something she did not do.

When we saw her in prison, we found out that she had confessed* to the crime! She had told the priest that she did it.

'Why did you confess?' asked Elizabeth. 'I believe you are innocent.'

'They told me that they did not believe me in court. They said I was to be hanged. They said that there was nothing that could save me. I was to die. Then the priest said that if I confessed, I would save my soul,' Justine wept. 'He said I would burn in hell unless I confessed before God.'

Elizabeth looked at me in horror.

Justine went on in a small voice, 'They went on and on at me. So I said I did it. Then they left me alone. Perhaps God will forgive me.'

'But you did nothing!' Elizabeth cried.

My throat went dry. I rushed out to see the judge. I tried to tell him what I knew. I started by saying that I knew Justine was innocent. I said she could not have done such a thing. I got out only a few words before he stopped me.

'Your desire to help and free this girl does you credit*, Frankenstein,' he said kindly but firmly. 'I know that she is like a member of the family. You are trying to protect her. But the girl murdered a child to steal a trinket*. She is evil and must be punished. She is guilty and will pay the penalty*.'

I begged, pleaded, and even shouted. But it was no use. I had no evidence, you see. They would not believe that another had killed William. They would not believe that Justine was innocent.

Later that day Justine was hanged for the murder of my brother William.

6 ∾ I MEET THE CREATURE AGAIN

Justine and William were dead. Their deaths were all because of me, because of what I had created. I was sure of it. I had meant well. I should have been proud of what I had done. The secret of life that was mine should have been a benefit* to all mankind. Instead, I was wretched* and filled with hate for the creature I had made. I went for a walk by the lake in the town. I felt I should throw myself in, yet I could not.

As fate would have it, I met Elizabeth walking too. Elizabeth said, 'Oh Victor! How sad you seem. Isn't it strange that evil can be all around us yet we do not know of it? But this time it has visited us in our home and become real. For the sake of a few jewels, it seems that Justine killed the child she had looked after for so long. But you say she was innocent. If that is true, then the killer must still be free. Justine's death has only added to the evil. Sometimes it seems to me that men are monsters thirsting for each other's blood.'

'I know she was innocent,' I said, but I could not bear to go on. I could not tell her how close to the truth her words were. I was the one who made the creature that had killed poor William. She would hate me forever if she knew that. I could not tell her and for that I was a shameful* coward.

I had to get away from the scene of the deaths. My father also felt a change of scene would help us to get over our grief. So Elizabeth and I departed for a brief tour to the mountains.

Later that week we were on a road that wound through the valley made by the river Arve. We saw great mountains overhanging us. We heard the sound of raging rivers and the dashing of waterfalls. As we went on, old castles peered down from high cliffs and cottages peeped out of forest. Yet all this was

made small by the mighty Alps*. Their white and shining domes towered above us. Capping it all was the vast peak of Mont Blanc* which overlooked the valley. That night I stayed awake watching the lightning play around the tops of the mountains.

The next morning was cloudy and cold. Elizabeth stayed in her room that day and I went out alone. I wished to climb the summit* of Montanvert*. There was a glacier* there. I hoped the view would improve my mood. Indeed, as I climbed the winding path, I felt myself rise above the worries of the last few weeks.

At noon, I reached the top. I sat on a rock above the clouds. All around was a sea of ice – the glacier. The surface was uneven, like frozen waves. Great cracks in the ice and bare rock thrusting upwards had made it a slow climb. It was with some surprise that I saw a figure bounding across the ice. He came at almost superhuman speed. He was quick and sure where I had been slow and careful.

As he came closer, I saw that he was huge, perhaps eight feet tall. He looked down on me with yellow eyes. I felt cold all over and I could hardly bear to look at that inhuman* face. And yet I knew him! It was the monster that I had created. I felt rage build up inside me. He stood with a look of bitter sadness on his face. I did not see this, as my hate and anger burst forth. I stood face-to-face with the monster I had made.

'You devil! How dare you come to me? Go away, you horrible creature. Or, better still, let me throw you down the mountain. I wish your death could bring William back to life!'

'All men hate those who are outcast*,' the demon* replied, 'so I knew you would welcome me with hate. I am cursed and yet you are my creator. You plan to kill me. But you are the one who gave me life. Can you play with life and death then? Perhaps I will feed myself on more of your friends!'

I was surprised to hear him talk like this, as if he could reason

and think. But my anger was too great to take any more notice of this.

'You monster! Hell is too mild a punishment for you. You talk of me as your creator. Come on then, let me put out the spark of life that I gave you.'

My rage knew no bounds* and I leapt at him. He stepped away as if I was a small child and held me at bay*.

'Be calm,' he begged. 'Listen to me before your hatred makes you attack me. I will defend myself. Remember, you have made me faster and more powerful than others. Oh, Frankenstein – I am your creature. I will be mild and tame before my lord if you will but listen. I was good and kind but my misery made me evil.'

'There can be no peace between us,' I shouted. 'Come on. We'll fight until one of us lies dead.'

'How can I make you listen? I was full of love for others, but now I am alone. You, my maker, hate me. The desert mountains and glaciers are my home. I have been alone in caves of ice, which

26

are kinder to me than my fellow humans. Try and pity me. Listen to my story and then judge me. Then, if you want to, you can destroy the work of your own hands.'

'Cursed be the hands that made you, even if that is to curse myself! I can't bear even to look at your vile form.'

'Then you don't have to look at me,' he said, placing his hands over my eyes so I could not see him. I think this must have been some kind of joke to him. I pushed his hands away with a shout. Yet I felt I should listen. Did he kill my brother? I had to know the truth. I followed him with a heavy heart. He seemed happy as we crossed the ice. The air was cold as we went into a hut. I sat by a fire that the creature had lit and he began his story.

7 ∾ THE CREATURE'S STORY: I LEARN ABOUT LIFE

I will tell you of the first moments of my life. I opened my eyes. The light hurt me. I did not know who or where I was but slowly I began to see things. I did not know then that you had made me. There was no one in the room. My throat was dry. I felt strange inside. Later I knew these two feelings as hunger and thirst. There was no yesterday for me, only now. There was only the moment before me. I had no memory of the past. Somehow my legs moved and I got up. My hands and feet felt big and clumsy.

I must have left the house. I think I may have seen you sleeping. I felt a warm feeling then, as if you were important to me. I think I may have tried to talk to you. But I could not speak then and did not know what to do. I must have left your house. I found out later that I had taken your cloak. I had no clothes on. Some deep part of me must have known that the cloak would keep me warm. I did not know what it was called then. All I know is that I had it with me when I began to understand things.

I found that I was outside in the forests and fields. Time had passed. The next thing I knew was the passing of light and dark. There was heat and cold. The cold came with the dark and the heat came with the light. The light would come slowly. Sometimes the dark would be lit up by a white glowing shape high above.

Later I knew these things as night, day, dawn, and the moon. I also learnt later that the bright thing that burnt me and then warmed me was a fire. I found one left by gypsies and slowly learnt how to tend* it, using dry branches for fire and wet branches for smoke. I found berries on trees. I could eat these but they would burn on the fire. On the other hand, nuts and roots tasted better when they were cooked.

In this way, I slowly learnt how to live. I learnt to understand the feelings of my body. The world around me began to make more sense. The snow on my feet was cold. I heard the birds singing and I tried to copy them.

At last, in my wanderings, I came upon a wonder*. It was a small hut and in front of it sat a man. Something inside me wanted to make contact. As I came near, he looked up. The man's mouth opened wide and he leapt up. He ran from me, making a loud noise.

I went inside the hut. It was dry and warm. I lay in the soft straw and wrapped myself in your cloak. I woke the next day and, taking some food, walked on to more huts. Some were larger, with laid out gardens. As I drew near all the children and some of the people yelled and shouted. Many ran away, but some came up to me. I lifted my hands to try and touch them. I felt tender* towards them. I wanted them to like me. I wanted to make some human contact with them. Some people picked up stones and threw them at me. Others hit me with sticks or spades. I was driven away, hurt and sore. I felt something wet on my cheeks. Water was coming from my eyes. Later, of course, I knew these were tears of sadness.

After a time I found a place to live. It was deep in the woods, not much more than sticks placed over tree trunks, but at least it was dry. One day I peered out of a hole in my hut. I had heard a sound. Through the rain-dripping branches I could see a young woman. She seemed gentle and kind. Unlike some of the others in the village, her clothes were old and worn. She carried a pail* of water. I followed her and she was joined by a young man. He took the pail from her and they came to a small house nearby. They worked in the yard, cutting wood. When they went inside, I crept up to the window. Looking in, I saw an old man sitting on a stool. The two young people made a meal, from hardly more than I could find myself in the woods. After the meal, the old man took out what I learnt later was a guitar. He played and the young woman sang.

Oh, what sweet sounds! I had never heard such sounds before. A mixture of joy and sadness filled my heart. Their song and clear love for each other was more than I could bear. I slipped away, but I knew I would come back.

8 ✤ I WATCH A FAMILY

I came back to the house the next day. I visited and watched them often. Soon I began to understand why they seemed sad. Their only food was a few vegetables in the garden and, like myself, berries and nuts from the forest. They had one cow which gave a little milk. They had few belongings. It also became clear that the old man was blind. Often the two younger people gave the old man their own food, leaving themselves nothing. I had been in the habit of taking some of their food for myself. When I saw how kind they were, I took my food from the forest again.

In fact, I found a way to help them. I saw how much time they spent in looking for wood for their fire. I collected this wood myself and was able to give them wood for days at a time. The first time the woman opened the door and saw the pile of wood, she cried out. The young man came running. They looked around, amazed. From then on they talked about a 'good spirit' who helped them.

Of course, I learnt this later as I began to find out about speech. I saw them make sounds at certain things. Soon, I saw

that these sounds were linked to things, like 'fire', 'milk', 'wood', and so on. Over time I learnt how to speak. I found out that the old man, de Lacey, was the father of Felix and Agatha. I wondered then, Frankenstein, who my father might be.

I learnt more than how to talk from this family. I also learnt about love, kindness to others, joy, laughter, sadness, and despair*. I learnt about many human feelings. I also saw how graceful and lovely the two young people were. Foolishly I thought that was how most humans were. One day I caught sight of myself in a pool of water. I drew back in horror! What a picture of ugliness I saw before me. If I had known then what my ugliness really meant, I would have been bitter indeed.

In spring there was a visitor. Another young lady, with long dark hair, arrived. Her name was Sophie and the others were overjoyed to see her. Sophie was in love with Felix. Sophie was Turkish and her parents did not want her to marry Felix. I also learnt that Sophie's father had been put in jail by the French. He had been a prisoner of war. Felix had freed him. As a result, de Lacey had all his money and land taken away. So he had fled the country and now lived in poverty*. Sophie had set out to find Felix.

At first it was hard to understand what Sophie was saying. Sophie took to reading histories with Felix so that she could improve her speech. Felix often spent some time talking about the books to Sophie. This also helped me to learn about the world. I learnt about the Greeks and Romans, families, wars, good, and evil. I learnt about how families and children lived and worked. I did not understand where my place was in all of this.

I learnt even more by watching the family. I had seen how, when Felix or Agatha had read to the old man, they would speak words which were shown by marks in the books. Now, as he read, Felix would stop and show Sophie the words in the books. He was teaching her to read as well. I paid close attention to this. Sometimes Felix would spell out the letters of the words. In this way I was, after a time, able to learn how to read. I had found a book in an inside pocket of your cloak. I did not know what it was. Now I could learn how to read it.

Imagine how I felt when I could read the book in your cloak. It was the journal[*] of how you created me! It must have been important to you for you to keep it so well hidden. At first I was pleased. You would be like a father to me. We might love each other as Felix and de Lacey did. Then I saw words like 'Cursed be the day I created this life' and 'My work has become a filthy thing.' I felt my heart sink. Could it be that you, my creator,

hated me? Was I filthy because I was dirty or did you think me unclean, like a demon?

I was sure that the people I watched would not feel that way. I had helped them, after all. They were kind and loving. Perhaps the old man, being blind, could be my friend. He would not see my ugliness. I would talk to him and then, when he was used to me, he could tell the others about me. Then they would learn to like me. Surely they would see past my ugliness to all the love I felt inside me.

So, one day, when only the old man was in, I knocked on the door.

'Come in,' said the old man.

'Pardon,' I said, 'but I am in need of rest. May I sit by your fire?'

'By all means,' he replied, 'but my family is out, and I am blind.'

'Don't worry,' I said, 'it is only rest I need.'

We carried on talking for a while. Then I turned to the heart of the matter. I said, 'I have come far and am lonely. There are some people that I know. I would like to be their friend.'

'Where do they live?' he said.

'Nearby.'

'What is the problem, then?'

'I fear that they will see me as a monster,' I said.

'Your voice seems kind enough,' he said. 'How can I help you?'

'If you can talk to these people…'

'I am sure they will welcome you,' the old man went on. 'If you tell me who you are I can talk to them.'

Just then I heard Felix, Agatha, and Sophie come to the door. They had returned sooner than I had hoped. I grabbed the old man's hand. 'Please, help me!' I cried.

'Who are you?' he said.

The others burst into the room. Sophie screamed with horror. Agatha shouted, 'Leave my father alone, you vile creature!' She tore his hands from my grasp. Felix struck out at me. I could have torn him limb from limb, but I just crouched as he hit and hit me. Finally, I could bear no more. I ran out and away, leaving their cries of 'Beast' and 'Monster' behind me.

9 ∾ I VOW REVENGE

As I ran, these thoughts came to me. I could no longer feel love inside me. I had been rejected*. Why did I live? Why did you not kill me when you first saw what you had created? All I wanted was to make friends. All I wanted was to feel the love that binds humans to each other. Yet my attempts to meet others had been crushed. I had so much goodwill* for these people. In return, they had hit and cursed me.

36

Slowly, I felt a feeling of rage build up inside me. I was a fool to think they would accept me. I had been cast* aside, now I wanted to tear them down and destroy them.

The next day I calmed down a little. I went back and hid near the house. I wanted to try and explain to the family that I meant them no harm. I just wanted to be friends. Then I heard people talking.

'We cannot find the monster,' a strange voice said.

'He has escaped us,' said a second voice. It was Felix. 'My father is in mortal danger*. The creature was trying to kill him!' I nearly burst out of my hiding place. I wanted to tell them it was not true. Yet I knew they would attack me again.

Later that week the family left. They feared another attack from me. They could not see that I meant no harm. I felt a terrible loneliness as they left. Then my sadness turned to despair and rage. A wind had risen that night. The lightning blasts

seemed to send me mad. I grabbed a branch of a tree that was burning, set alight by the lightning. Screaming, I ran and thrust the burning branch into the house. Soon the house was ablaze[*]. The wind fanned the flames. I burnt down the house which had given me such pleasure and warmth. As the house burnt, I felt all my love for humans burning too.

In a kind of dream, I wandered off. For the next few days I kept to the dark parts of the wood. I could not bear the sunshine. Then, one day, I heard cries from nearby. I ran and came to a river. A little girl was being swept down by the current[*]. Without thinking, I dived into the river. I dragged her to the shore. She was senseless, but alive. I carried her in my arms. I saw her father running along the bank, crying out. A second chance, I said to myself. Even if I am a monster, he will see that I have saved his little girl. I held her up to him.

'Let her be, you vile monster,' he shouted. He grabbed the girl from my arms and raced off. I went to follow him, to explain. He put her down and took up his gun, which was slung over his shoulder. He fired, and I felt a pain in my arm as he ran off.

So, this is how I was repaid for my help. My reasons had been good and kind. Now I felt anger and rage. The pain from the bullet made me full of hatred. I vowed[*] revenge on all humans.

I was lucky that the bullet went into the fleshy part of my arm. It passed out of the other side. Over the next few weeks my wound got better. From your journal, I knew that you and your family lived in Geneva. I had learnt something of places and towns from the books Felix had read to Sophie. I went to see if I could find you. Late one night I found myself close to a park in some woods. I saw a little boy who seemed to be lost. He seemed kind and gentle. My rage had been building over the last few weeks, but now, perhaps, I had a third chance. This young boy would not have such fixed ideas about people. He would see past my ugliness

to the love beneath. His family would also be grateful to have him returned. I stepped out from behind a tree and, as gently as I could, took the boy's arm. He turned around. When he saw me, his face went pale and he opened his mouth and screamed loudly.

'Why do you cry?' I said. 'I do not intend* to hurt you. Are you lost?'

'Let me go,' he yelled, and twisted away from me. 'Ugly monster, you will eat me and tear me to bits.'

'No, I mean to help.'

'Let me go,' he said, and kicked me. 'I will tell my father, everyone knows him.' I began to feel angry then, and the boy went on, 'My father is Mr Frankenstein. He will punish you. Let me go.'

When I heard your name – the name of my creator – I felt a red rage come over me. You who hated me! You who could not be my father. It was your fault I was hated by others. I thought the boy was your son. I thought this was the son you loved. You had cast me out but now I would get my revenge. Perhaps the pain you would feel if I hurt this boy would make you understand what I had felt. I grasped* the boy around the throat. My large hands gripped tightly. Then the boy lay dead at my feet. I felt a strange joy, at first. I had got my revenge. Then I saw something shining at the boy's neck. It was a locket. I pulled it off him and looked at the picture. It was a lovely woman, so gentle and soft. Now I felt that I was truly a monster. I was ashamed and sorry. I could not keep the locket.

Later that night, I came across a barn. Thinking to spend the night, I went in. There was a young woman sleeping there. She looked so lovely. I hated her for her beauty. Why could I not have a friend like this? I knew that if I woke her she would be scared. She would scream and call others to beat me. This made me angry again. Perhaps she would suffer if she somehow took the

40

blame for the boy's death. So, I put the locket into her pocket and went out into the night.

10 ∾ FRANKENSTEIN'S STORY: I MAKE A SECOND CREATURE

You can imagine how I felt, Walton. I had been right about William. The creature I had created was a murderer! At this point the creature looked at me. When I said nothing he went on.

'For the next few nights I visited the same place.'

'I saw you there one night,' I said, as rage grew inside me. 'I knew you had killed William.'

'It is easy for you to hate me,' he said, seeing the look on my face. 'You know nothing of how I have felt. I am rejected. I am alone. But you must do something for me. I must have a friend

41

who will be happy to be with me. I need someone who will understand me. Someone I can talk to. Someone who will not be frightened by what I look like. You can make someone like me. You must make a mate* for me. A female to be my companion*.'

At these words the anger I felt, at hearing how he had killed poor William, burst forth. 'I will not!' I shouted. 'Nothing you do to me will make me. I shall never make another creature as horrible as you. Go away and leave me!'

'You are wrong,' replied the creature. 'Is it my fault I am like I am? You would destroy me. Is that not murder too? How can I respect humans when they attack me? All I ask is this small thing. I beg you, my creator, if you have any feeling left, help me.'

I looked at him. Perhaps I was at fault*. He had not asked to be created, after all. Perhaps William's murder and Justine's hanging were as much my fault as his. I had never thought that the life I had made might have feelings of his own. Seeing my face change, the creature went on.

'If you agree you shall never see us again. We shall live in the wilds. I shall never do evil deeds* again. I will be happy. I will have someone to love and will be loved.'

My heart was swayed by his words. Yes, the monster had killed. I could not bear to look at him. Yet he had tried to love and had been treated badly. I could try and understand him.

'So you promise to leave Europe forever?' I said.

'I swear by the sun and the sky,' he cried.

'Very well,' I said, 'I shall make you a female companion.'

'Go, start your work and I shall watch.' So saying, he turned and fled up the mountain.

On our return to Geneva, I thought long and hard. My father reminded me of my promise to marry Elizabeth. I knew I had to go to England to get help for my work. There were some professors at Oxford who had been studying life forces. I told my

father that I had to travel, but I did not say why. I said goodbye to Elizabeth and promised to marry her on my return.

Henry Clerval came with me on my journey. He did not know my reasons, but wanted to see England. When we arrived in England, I went to Oxford. I talked to the professors who had worked in Chemistry. This time I wanted to do better. I would make the female beautiful. I would not make the same mistakes. I was full of hope again. I spent some time studying, but I kept my reasons secret from the professors. Then I went to find somewhere remote* to start my work. I did not want anyone to know what I was doing. The secret must be kept. No one must see what I was doing.

We went on to Scotland, to Edinburgh, where Clerval had some friends. From here I planned to travel north where there were fewer people. I needed to work alone. Clerval did not like me going on alone. But, at last, he agreed to stay in Edinburgh. He told me not to be away for long, or he would come and find me.

I left my friend and went north to the highlands of Scotland. From there I went on by boat, to the Orkney Islands*. I rented a house on one of the islands. There were only three other houses on the whole island. It was very lonely and remote.

In this bleak*, windswept place I started my work. The sea crashed around the island as I unpacked all the horrible things I needed. I had all the body parts and materials. The work, as before, was hard and disgusting. Soon I had everything ready for the electrical spark from lightning. All I needed was a storm to give me the power for that spark of light.

As I waited, I began to think about my life and what I was doing. I was still thinking when the moon rose. It was a bright full moon that night. It shone in through the window. The pale body of my new creation lay on the table. Was this the right thing to do? Would the woman be as evil as the man I had made?

Perhaps they would hate each other. What if they killed together? They might urge each other to do more and more terrible deeds.

What if they had children? A race* of monsters could roam the world. What if they were all evil murderers? Humankind* could be under attack. People would curse me as the creator of these terrors.

11 ∽ ANOTHER DEATH

As I sat there, I felt eyes watching me! With a start*, I turned to the window. There, in the light of the moon, a demon face peered in. He had followed me. Now he looked in to see my work. A grin split open his face. I cannot tell you how awful that look was. It was brutal*, yet full of glee* as it saw the creature laid out on the table.

I felt anger build up inside me. How could I even think of creating a second creature like this one? It was wrong. Suddenly, I knew it was wrong. In a fit of madness I attacked the thing on the table. I tore it apart, limb from limb. I hacked and pulled, I slashed and cut. In moments I had destroyed months of work. Bits of flesh and bone lay on the floor. All my wires and switches were broken.

There was a howl of anger from the window. Then the creature could no longer be seen. There was a crash as he burst open the door as if it was matchwood*. The monster raged into the room, his yellow eyes burning.

'Why have you broken your promise?' he shouted. 'Why have you destroyed the work that you began?'

'Yes, I have broken my promise! Never will I make a creature like you again,' I said. I went on, 'My moment of weakness has passed.'

The monster cried out in rage, 'I have a right not to be alone!

I have tried hard to love but you have crushed me. Humankind has rejected me. I have the right to someone who will love me for myself. Why do you have the right to be happy and not me?'

'Be silent, you devil,' I said. 'My mind is made up. Leave me.'

'So,' the monster replied, seeing that I meant what I said, 'I will go, but I am powerful. Remember these words – I shall be with you on your wedding night.'

I leapt forward to grab him. He pushed me away and I fell to the floor. The next thing I saw in the moonlight was his boat, which shot across the water like an arrow. The monster was soon lost in the darkness.

The night wore on. I sat lost in my thoughts. I kept thinking of his words, 'I will be with you on your wedding night.' I wept bitter tears. Then I decided I had to get on with my life. I would return to Geneva, marry Elizabeth, and put all this behind me.

Yet there was one thing I had to do. All the bits and pieces of my work lay around the room. I could not let anyone else see it. All my equipment was there too. I could not risk someone else using my work to create another monster.

So, at three o'clock in the morning, I loaded all the equipment into a boat. I set out over the dark sea. I sailed about four miles out and threw my vile cargo* overboard. With a gurgle it sank into the cold depths. No one else would be able to copy my work now.

That night seemed to be a cursed one. Soon a storm blew up, and I was cast to the mercy of* the waves. How my boat did not sink I do not know. I could hardly hold the rudder* to steer it. At last, I was thrown onto a shore. I cried tears of joy to be back on land and fell into a fitful* sleep. When I woke next, the sun was shining on my face. I looked up and saw a group of people staring down at me. They all looked angry.

'Where am I?' I asked.

'You will soon be in the hands of the Law,' one of the men said.

'The Law?' I said. 'Am I not a free man?'

There was a low growl from the group. Three men grabbed me and I was dragged roughly onto my feet. I did not know what was going on as I was pushed and pulled about. It soon became clear, as I was taken to Mr Kirwin, the local judge.

He told me what had happened. The night before, the body of a young man had been found cast up on the beach. At first it seemed as though he had drowned. Then the black marks of fingers were found on his neck. He had been strangled to death. On hearing this, I felt my knees give way. It was the monster! Once again someone had died as a result of my creation.

Worse was to come. I was taken to see the body of the young man. I looked down and saw the lifeless body of my friend, Henry Clerval. I gasped and fell to the ground, weeping.

Because I had been found in a boat on a nearby beach, they thought that I had come across the young man at sea. When they saw how I knew him and wept, they took that as evidence that I had killed him. I was thrown into prison. There I would wait to be tried* for the murder of my friend Henry!

It was all too much for me. I fell ill. I spent hours just staring into space. I had become a kind of madman. The people had found my address from papers I had in my pocket. They wrote to my family and at last my father came to see me. I was so happy to see him. He came to the trial with me. It turned out that Henry had been killed the day before I came to shore. The medical evidence had proved the time of his death. Someone had seen me in the Orkney Islands at the time poor Henry had been killed. This proved that I could not have been the murderer. At last, I was set free.

12 ∾ THE MONSTER'S REVENGE

As we made our way back to Geneva, I had terrible dreams. Sometimes I saw the bodies of William, Justine, and Henry. I awoke after these dreams screaming that I had killed them. Sometimes I saw the face and yellow eyes of the monster. Then I woke in a cold sweat, fearful for my life. I still could not tell my father what I had done. Surely Elizabeth would not want to marry me, I thought. Then I had a letter from her.

Dearest Victor,

I am so sorry to hear of Henry's death. There has been so much death and sorrow. Let us hope we can now put it all behind us.

I'm looking forward to seeing you very much. You have been away for so long. I hope you do not love someone else. We have been promised to each other since we were young. I want nothing but your happiness.

As for me, I do still love you. But I can only marry you if you love me too. Think about these things and talk to me on your return.

With all my love
Elizabeth

At once my spirits rose*. Sweet Elizabeth would help me make sense of my life. I wrote, telling her that I loved her too. As soon as I returned to Geneva I took her in my arms. Elizabeth was still lovely, but looked thinner. She had been worried about me. I seemed to be so wrapped up in my thoughts. Sometimes she had thought me a little mad. But now we could make a life together. We could try and forget all the terrible things and be happy. We planned to marry as soon as possible.

As the day of the wedding came near, I began to worry. The monster's last words kept coming back to me. Elizabeth saw my worries. She thought that I was having second thoughts about marrying. I could not tell the reason – all I could say was that I still wanted to marry her and that I loved her.

At last the day came and we were married. That evening we went to stay at a hotel on the other side of the lake. The boat trip was peaceful and I felt that my troubles were behind me. Perhaps the monster would not come back. I tried to put him out of my mind and pretend that nothing had happened. I should have learnt by now that this was a foolish thing to do.

Later that evening a storm began to build up. I had felt calm all day, but now began to worry. The words 'I shall be with you on your wedding night' kept pounding like a gong in my head. I had a dagger and pistol with me. Now I was glad of them. The creature would not find me such an easy target! I told Elizabeth that I wanted to go for a walk. I really wanted to check that the creature was not in the grounds.

Elizabeth went to our room. I walked out into the wind, which flung rain into my face. I walked into the grounds. I could not see much so I went inside again. I walked around the hotel. Then I heard a sound which chilled my blood. A scream! It came from our room. I froze for an instant*. Then I rushed upstairs. I burst into the room. There, on the bed, lay Elizabeth. She was lying across the bed with her head thrown back. Her hair hung down over the side of the bed and her limbs were lifeless. Around her neck I saw those dreadful marks – black marks where fingers had crushed her throat.

I held her to me, but it was too late. My new wife was dead. I fell to my knees with a wail* of despair. I thought the monster had meant to kill me! As if to mock the act of creating the monster, lightning lit up the room. The curtains at the window blew inwards. There, etched* in the light of the storm, stood the creature. A grin was spread over that devilish face. He pointed to the body and jeered*, 'I will be with you on your wedding night.'

I took out my pistol. In a rage I fired at him, but it was too late. He had gone. The shot brought others rushing into the room. I fell to the ground and wept bitter tears.

I wept all that night. Then, with the new day, a terrible thought came to me. My father and brother! Even now they might be having their necks crushed by the monster! I rushed back to Geneva as fast as I could. My father and Ernest were safe. Yet, as I told them of Elizabeth's death, my father seemed to shrink into himself. All the deaths had been too much for him. He died soon after, of a broken heart I am sure.

This time I knew I had to tell the judge. I told him the full story. I tried to be calm as he looked at me strangely. How could he believe such a story? I finished by saying, 'You must try and find this creature. He must be punished. I fear he will kill again.'

I could tell he did not believe me but he did ask, 'Well, how

can we catch such a creature? If he is as strong, fast, and cunning as you say we will not find him.' I left, knowing the law could not, or would not, help. From that moment I began my travels. I would find the creature myself!

First, I visited the cemetery* where my family was buried. William and Elizabeth lay side by side. All was silent as I stood over the graves. I spoke aloud. 'I vow by the spirits of the earth that I will have revenge. Help me, spirits, so that he may feel the despair that now torments me*.' As I spoke, I heard mocking laughter. It rang loud and long in my ears.

Then I heard a voice, a well-known and hated voice. He said, 'Now I am happy. You shall live in misery. You will feel all the pain that I have felt. I am content[*].'

I ran to where the voice came from, but he had gone. Then began months of hardship[*] and travel. I followed the monster. Always, just when I seemed to have lost him, I found a sign. I saw him get onto a boat bound for the Black Sea[*]. I found his huge footprint in the snows of Russia. I saw some marks he had carved in a tree: 'Come on, my enemy, keep up!' Later I knew he was teasing me. He could have escaped but wanted me to follow. He wanted my torment to last. He left a trail for me on purpose. He wanted to be found.

The last message I had from him was as follows: 'I seek the everlasting ice. Prepare yourself. Bring food and furs. Your work has just begun.'

So that is how I came to be here, my dear Walton. I followed him to the North Pole. I came by sledge, pulled by dogs, as he had done. Some of my dogs died and I was cold and hungry. Yet I nearly had him! He was only just ahead of me. Then the ice cracked open and the sea surged out. My sledge and the remaining dogs were sucked under. I scrambled onto the small iceberg where you found me.

God forgive me, Walton. I am ill now, but if he should come, beware. His words will win you over to his side. Do not trust him, he is evil.

13 ∾ WALTON'S LETTER TO HIS SISTER, MARGARET, CONTINUES

So, Margaret, you have heard the terrible tale of Frankenstein and his monster. Perhaps you can hardly believe it. I would not have believed it myself apart from two things. The first was that I

had seen the creature, the second that even a madman could not have made up such a story! When he had finished, I said, 'You must not let your secret stay with you, Frankenstein. Tell me how you created this man.'

'Are you mad?' he said angrily. 'No one must try such a thing again. Have you not learnt anything from the awful things that have happened? We must not play at gods.' He then looked at all the notes I had made about his story. He crossed out any details that gave a hint* as to how the monster was made.

Over the next few days Frankenstein's health became worse. The ice was beginning to crack now. The ship was slowly freeing itself from it. Frankenstein lay with his eyes closed. His skin was pale. I sat by his side. I had to lean close to hear him talking.

'I shall die soon, Walton. What shall I think about my life? I wanted to make an intelligent being. Should I have taken greater care in my duty to it? He tried to love but others would not let him. Should I have made a mate for him? Should he now be destroyed? Was he evil, or did he learn that from humans?'

I had no answer to these questions. Then he gripped me with his hand. 'No! I was right, Walton. I should not have helped him. Before I told my story, I said I would ask you to do something for me. Now is the time for me to ask it. You must promise me one thing.'

'What would that be?' I asked, taken aback* by his sudden anger.

'You must promise to kill the creature. You must take up my burden*. You must seek him and destroy him! Promise me, Walton.'

Before I could reply, he began to choke. It was as if his last strength had been drawn out of him. He tried to speak, but could not. He pressed my hand again and died.

As I write this letter, Margaret, I still do not know what to make of it all. Wait! I hear a sound in the cabin. I will return to this letter shortly…

Margaret, I can hardly believe what has just happened. I went into Frankenstein's cabin and a massive form stood over the bed. He was looking at Frankenstein's body, his long hair hanging down. He reached out a hand – it was huge. He heard me come in. He turned to leave the cabin, his yellow eyes glaring at me. He was loathsome*. I looked at him. Frankenstein had wanted me to kill him. Could I do it? I began to reach for my pistol.

Then he spoke, almost as if I was not there.

'This is my victim*, yet he was my father. He created me, yet I hate him. He cannot forgive me now he is so cold!'

I was amazed at how such a vile-looking creature could speak in such an intelligent way.

'Your sorrow is too late now, creature,' I said.

'What do you know?' he said. 'Do you think the groans of those I killed were music to my ears? No! I hated myself and pitied Frankenstein. Now he is my last victim.'

'You feel no pity,' I shouted, 'only sorrow that you did not kill him yourself.'

He turned to me and said, 'Once again I find no love for me amongst humankind. Why do you not hate those that hurt me when I reached out to them? I had hoped to be one of you, but now I am alone. Have no fear. You will not see me again. I am not worthy to live. I intend to make a great fire and I shall cast myself into it.'

I did not know what to say. Would the creature really kill himself or is he, even now, out in the ice waiting for a time to come back to our cities? As I stood, staring at him, he jumped out of the cabin window. He landed on an ice raft. Soon the wind and waves carried him away. He was lost in the darkness and distance. ❧

58

GLOSSARY

3 **St Petersburg** city in Russia
frozen wastes ice-covered land
with no plants or houses

4 **overboard** off the side of the
ship
aboard onto the ship
task job
barely hardly; with difficulty

5 **mankind** the whole human race
orphan child whose parents
have died
foster parents a couple who look
after a child who has lost
his/her parents

7 **create** make something new
university place of advanced
learning and study
Chemistry the study of how
different substances react with
each other
ebb and flow movement back
and forth, like the sea
Professor teacher at a university
driven forced along (by desire)

8 **mocked** made fun of
texts books, writings

9 **Biology** the study of life
frame body
decayed rotted away
straying wandering away

10 **slabs** stone tables (for laying out
bodies)
organs parts inside the body
(liver, heart, lungs, etc.)
meddle interfere

12 **creation** something that has
been created
vessels arteries and veins which
carry blood around the body
corpse a dead body

16 **locket** a small case holding a
picture, worn around the neck

17 **murky** dark and gloomy

18 **evidence** information which
makes something clear

19 **events had overtaken me** what
actually happened moved faster
than I could

20 **housekeeper** a person employed
to look after a house
trial a test in a court of law
courtroom the room where a
trial takes place
lawyer person who knows about
the law and argues in a court

22 **barn** a large building on a farm
where animals or crops are kept
confessed admitted to doing
something

23 **does you credit** shows that you
are a good person
trinket a small item that a
person values
pay the penalty be punished for
what she has done
benefit a help; something that is
good
wretched very unhappy

24 **shameful** causing shame, disgrace

25 **Alps** mountains in central Europe
Mont Blanc the highest mountain in the Alps
summit the top of the mountain
Montanvert a mountain in the Alps.
glacier a wide, solid river of ice
inhuman not human; cruel
outcast someone who has been pushed out from normal society
demon devil

26 **knew no bounds** had no limits; was as big as it could be
held me at bay stopped me from reaching and attacking him

28 **tend** look after

29 **a wonder** something strange and wonderful
tender soft, loving
pail a bucket

32 **despair** the loss of all hope
in poverty with very little money and few possessions

33 **journal** a diary, a record of events

36 **rejected** turned away, refused by other people
goodwill positive feeling

37 **cast** thrown
in mortal danger in danger of his life

38 **ablaze** on fire

current strong flow of water in the river
vowed promised to carry out

40 **intend** want, mean
grasped gripped

42 **mate** a partner of the other sex
companion a friend
at fault to blame
deeds actions

44 **remote** far away
Orkney Islands islands off the north coast of Scotland
bleak empty, bare, unfriendly

45 **race** a group of people of the same type
Humankind the whole human race
start sudden movement, out of surprise
brutal cruel; like a brute
glee enjoyment
matchwood light wood like that used for matches

48 **cargo** a load carried by a ship or boat
to the mercy of to the power of (to spare or destroy)
rudder a flat piece of wood used for steering a boat
fitful restless, in short bursts

49 **tried** put on trial

50 **my spirits rose** I felt happier

52 **instant** moment
wail a loud cry
etched drawn in hard outline
jeered said in a mocking way

54 **cemetery** the place where dead people are buried
    torments me makes me suffer

55 **content** happy, satisfied
    hardship things which are hard to bear
    Black Sea an inland sea between south-east Europe and Asia

57 **hint** a clue

taken aback surprised in an unpleasant way
burden load; a thing which is carried

58 **loathsome** horrible, vile
    victim someone who has suffered because of some cause or person

C000228641

100 WALKS IN
Northumberland

The Crowood Press

First published in 1992 by
The Crowood Press Ltd
Ramsbury,
Marlborough
Wiltshire SN8 2HR

Revised edition 1994

This impression 1998

British Library Cataloguing-in-Publication Data
A catalogue record from this book is
available from the British Library.

ISBN 1 85223 676 0

The author acknowledges the assistance of the leaflets produced by Allendale Parish
Council in researching some of the walks in this volume.

All maps by Sharon Perks

Cover picture by John Cleare

Typeset by Carreg Limited, Ross-on-Wye, Herefordshire

Printed in Great Britain by Redwood Books, Trowbridge, Wiltshire

compiled by

CHARLIE EMETT

CONTENTS

36. Steel Rigg and Hotbank 4m (6.4km)
37. Old Bewick and Blawearie 4m (6.4km)
38. Park Burnfoot and Bellister Castle 4m (6.4km)
39. Housesteads, King's Wicket and Hotbank 4m (6.4km)
40. Kirknewton and College Burn 4m (6.4km)
41. The Harthope Valley and North Middleton 4m (6.4km)
42. The Duchess Trail $4^1/_4$m (6.8km)
43. Holy Island $4^1/_2$m (7.2km)
44. Craster and Howick $4^1/_2$m (7.2km)
45. The Harthope Valley and Old Middleton $4^1/_2$m (7.2km)
46. Sparty Lea and Swinhope $4^1/_2$m (7.2km)
47. Happy Valley $4^1/_2$m (7.2km)
48. The Hope and Cose Hole $4^1/_2$m (7.2km)
49. Dunstan Steads and Craster $4^1/_2$m (7.2km)
50. Hartside and Cobden $4^1/_2$m (7.2km)
51. Once Brewed and Winshield's Crags $4^1/_2$m (7.2km)
52. Low Prudhoe and Horsley 5m (8km)
53. Walltown and the Loddams 5m (8km)
54. Debdon Road End and Rothbury 5m (8km)
55. Elsdonburn and the Scottish Border 5m (8km)
56. Walltown and Greenhead 5m (8km)
57. Ingram and Cochrane Pike 5m (8km)
58. Mounthooly and The Schil 5m (8km)
59. Wooler and Weetwood Moor 5m (8km)
60. Alwinton and Kidlandlee $5^1/_2$m (8.8km)
61. Holburn Grange and Fawcet Hill $5^1/_2$m (8.8km)
62. Rothbury and Gorleigh Moor $5^1/_2$m (8.8km)
63. Clennell and Puncherton $5^1/_2$m (8.8km)
64. The Harthope Valley and Broadstruther $5^1/_2$m (8.8km)
65. Studdon and Sinderhope $5^1/_2$m (8.8km)
66. Wooler and Fowberry 6m (9.6km)
67. High Humbleton and Gleadscleugh 6m (9.6km)
68. Wylam and Newburn Bridge 6m (9.6km)
69. Wooler and Fowberry Moor 6m (9.6km)
70. South Middleton and Threestone Burn 6m (9.6km)
71. The Rothbury Terraces 6m (9.6km)
72. Budle Bay $6^1/_2$m (10.4km)

73. Allenbanks $6^1/_2$m (10.4km)
74. Once Brewed and Vindolanda 7m (11.2km)
75. Allendale and Catton 7m (11.2km)
76. Humbleton Burn and Hellpath 7m (11.2km)
77. Steel Rigg and Housesteads 7m (11.2km)
78. Craster to Beadnell Harbour 7m (11.2km)
79. Rothbury Line and Wannie Line 7m (11.2km)
80. Hartside and Little Dod 7m (11.2km)
81. Bewick Moor and Harehope $7^1/_2$m (12km)
82. Craster and Howick Hall 8m (12.8km)
83. Alwinton and Shillmoor 8m (12.8km)
84. Alnmouth to Craster 8m (12.8km)
85. Blanchland and Slaley Forest 9m (14.4km)
86. Kielder Water 9m (14.4km)
87. Blanchland Moor $9^1/_2$m (15.2km)
88. Wylam and Greenside 10m (16km)
89. East Allendale and Cowshill 10m (16km)
90. Pauperhaugh Bridge to Felton 10m (16km)
91. Beadnell Harbour to Budle 10m (16km)
92. Windy Gyle $10^1/_2$m (16.8km)
93. Derwent Railway $10^1/_2$m (16.8km)
94. The Cheviot 11m (17.6km)
95. Tom Tallon's Crag 11m (17.6km)
96. Salters Road 12m (19.2km)
97. The Schil 14m (22.4km)
98. The West and East Allen's Meeting 14m (22.4km)
99. Housesteads to Bellingham 15m (24km)
100. The Border Ridge $27^1/_2$m (44km)

PUBLISHER'S NOTE

We very much hope that you enjoy the routes presented in this book, which has been compiled with the aim of allowing you to explore the area in the best possible way – on foot.

We strongly recommend that you take the relevant map for the area, and for this reason we list the appropriate Ordnance Survey maps for each route. Whilst the details and descriptions given for each walk were accurate at time of writing, the countryside is constantly changing, and a map will be essential if, for any reason, you are unable to follow the given route. It is good practice to carry a map and use it so that you are always aware of your exact location.

We cannot be held responsible if some of the details in the route descriptions are found to be inaccurate, but should be grateful if walkers would advise us of any major alterations. Please note that whenever you are walking in the countryside you are on somebody else's land, and we must stress that you should *always* keep to established rights of way, and *never* cross fences, hedges or other boundaries unless there is a clear crossing point.

Remember the country code:

Enjoy the country and respect its life and work
Guard against all risk of fire
Fasten all gates
Keep dogs under close control
Keep to public footpaths across all farmland
Use gates and stiles to cross field boundaries
Leave all livestock, machinery and crops alone
Take your litter home
Help to keep all water clean
Protect wildlife, plants and trees
Make no unnecessary noise

The walks are listed by length – from approximately 1 to 12 miles – but the amount of time taken will depend on the fitness of the walkers and the time spent exploring any points of interest along the way. Nearly all the walks are circular and most offer recommendations for refreshments.

Good walking.

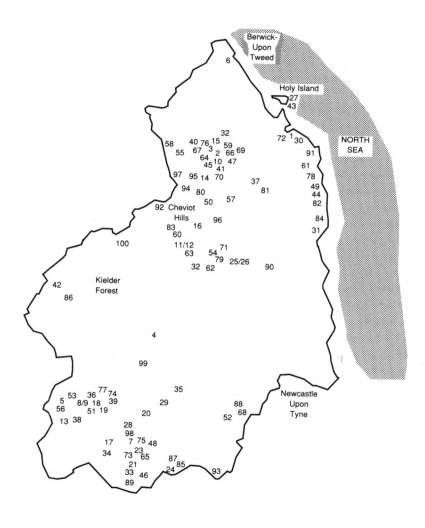

Walk 1   **BUDLE AND BUDLE POINT**   2m (3.2km)

Maps: OS Sheets Landranger 75; Pathfinder NU 13/23.

*The view of the bay and its wildlife make this short walk an
absolute must.*

Start: At 155351, the crossroads in Budle.

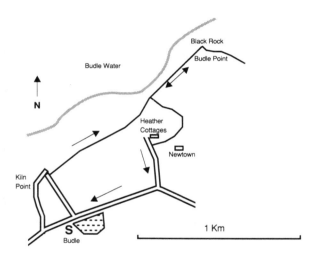

From the footpath notice on the north side of the crossroads go along the track towards
the bay, going through a gate and passing cottages on the left. At the end of the track
turn right, along the high water mark, passing some exposed limestone and going
towards Heather Cottages. Just before the Cottages, leave the tideline along a path to
the right of a dune and to the left of some cottages. The path bears to the left of a small
building and crosses a flat area to go back to the tideline between loose sandy slopes.
Go to the old quay ahead for a good view of the outer bay. Continue north-east along
the high water mark as far as **Black Rock**. Retrace your steps to the quay and turn
left, inland, along a faint sandy track to a caravan park. Turn left at the park, along a
path to a gun emplacement – 1940's vintage. Go to the right of it and immediately
sharp right to reach the edge of a golf course. Go to the right of the greens and right

again to a gateway leading to a surfaced road. Go left to reach a gate with caravans and Heather Cottages to the right. Turn left and continue towards a gate leading to a main road. Turn right to return to the starting point.

POINTS OF INTEREST:

Black Rock – The rock is a large slab of dolerite, part of the Whin Sill that forms Kittling Hill and Bamburgh, just round the headland. It makes a marvellous observation point; the great sweep of Ross Back Sands leading the eye to Holy Island and Lindisfarne Castle.

During the summer and early autumn swallows and sand martins are evident in large numbers near Budle. The sand martins nest in a cliff of boulder clay, deposited during the last Ice Age. The dunes in front of the cliff are covered in plants such as sea rocket which, together with the dune grasses, sand couch and lyme grass, hold the dunes together. They are known as 'dune fluking' plants, and do an important job.

Walk 2 HUMBLETON BURN AND WOOLER COMMON $2^1/_2$m (4km)

Maps: OS Sheets Landranger 75; Pathfinder NT 82/92.

Beginning with a short climb and continuing as an easy, pleasant walk on good paths.

Start: At 977272, the bridge at Humbleton Burn Picnic Place.

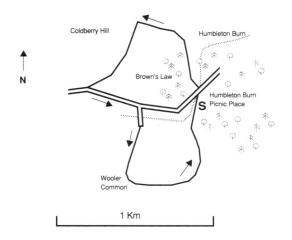

Coldberry Hill

Humbleton Burn

N

Brown's Law

Humbleton Burn
Picnic Place

S

Wooler
Common

1 Km

Cross the bridge out of the Picnic Place and turn right, along a burnside footpath. A yellow flower with red blotches, the monkey flower, grows here because it likes wet places by shallow streams.

As the path starts to climb the hill a rectangular depression is passed to the left. It was here, during the First World War, that the militia would come and practice rifle shooting. The targets were hoisted from behind the nearer ridge. The soldiers down the valley shot at them, and the bullets buried themselves harmlessly in the second, larger ridge. In old guide books the area is referred to as 'The Targets'. On reaching a gate, go through it and continue ahead. Here the sheep are usually Cheviot, short compact sheep. They are white faced, hornless and usually have a dip in the back. The breed is well-suited to lower upland grazings and when mated with a Border Leicester ram produce Scots half-bred lambs. The Border Leicester stands high off the ground, has a white face with a Roman nose and no horns. Its ears lie forward and it has ragged wool.

Go through a second gate and turn left. Follow the fence on the left to reach a gate, and continue downhill, through gorse, just below a line of trees on the right. The sunken parallel tracks on the right were probably made by cattle being driven across the hill in olden days. Turn left at a road and go along it for a short distance before turning right along a broad, grassy track to reach a burn. Go through a gate and take the path up the right-hand, lower, slopes of the hill, bearing left at the top to pass Wooler Common Farm on the right. Continue ahead to pick up a track and a fence on the right. After 100 yards bear left, away from the track, and descend gradually along another track to reach a stile. Now walk back to the picnic area.

POINTS OF INTEREST:
The broad, green track to the burn short of Wooler Common Farm is part of a local drove road once used to drive cattle to summer grazing grounds or to market. The width of the track allowed for grazing en route. In some places these old roads were called 'Streets'.

REFRESHMENTS:
Available at Wooler, about a mile away.

Walk 3   HUMBLETON BURN AND BROWN'S LAW   2¹/₂m (4km)

Maps: : OS Sheets Landranger 75; Pathfinder NT 82/92.

A short uphill climb at the outset followed by an easy pleasant walk along the lower slopes of hills.

Start: At 977272, the Humbleton Burn Picnic Place.

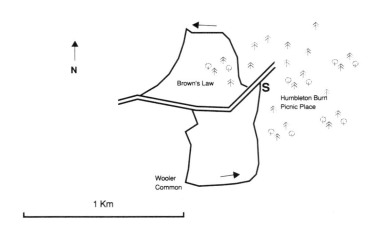

From the picnic area cross a bridge and follow a footpath on the right, staying close to Humbleton Burn and climbing steadily. The rectangular depression in the ground on the left is where, during World War I, the militia practised rifle shooting. Targets were hoisted from behind the nearer and smaller of two ridges, the soldiers shot at them and the bullets buried themselves harmlessly in the second ridge.

This path leads through a gate and on to a second gate. Turn left and follow the fence on the left to reach a gate. Continue downhill, going through gorse and staying just below a line of trees on the right. On reaching a road turn left for a short distance, then go down a broad grassy track to reach the burn. This is the land of the Cheviot Sheep. They are generally white-faced, hornless and have a dip in the back. Once known as the 'Long Breed', today's Cheviots are shorter and more compact. The breed is ideally suited to lower upland grazing. Cheviot ewes, mated with Border Leicester rams, produce Scots half-bred lambs.

Go through a gate and follow the path up the right-hand, lower slopes of the hill, bearing left at the top to pass Wooler Common Farm. Wooler townspeople had rights of pasturage on Wooler Common until it was enclosed in 1867. At that time the nine freeholders received allotments of less than one acre each.

Pass the farmhouse and walk ahead to pick up a track and a fence on the right. After 100 yards bear left, away from the track, and descend along another track to a stile. Go over and walk back to the picnic area.

POINTS OF INTEREST:

This area is noted for its whinchats, migrant birds which spend their winters around the Mediterranean or in Africa. They breed in areas without bushes, but with thistles and bracken on which they can perch and sing.

Walk 4   **HARESHAW LINN**   3m (4.8km)

Maps: OS Sheets Landranger 80; Pathfinder NY 88/98.

A superb walk, noted for its deciduous woodland and its interesting flora and fauna.

Start: At 840835, the Hareshaw Linn car park at Bellingham.

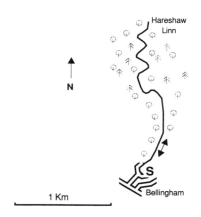

From the car park follow an unsurfaced road from Bellingham signposted 'Public Footpath: Hareshaw Linn'. Go through a small gate to the left of a building and along a track to a second small gate to the left of a building and along a track to a second small gate. Continue along a broad path with a fence on the right, soon bearing left between **hillocks**. At the end of the path go through a small gate leading to a wood. Now follow a clear, partly cobbled path that descends to a footbridge over a stream. Stay on the path, crossing five more bridges until the waterfall, **Hareshaw Linn**, is reached. As there are no escape routes from the valley the return is along the outward path. However, as this is one of the most delightful short walks in Northumberland this is hardly a problem.

POINTS OF INTEREST:

Hillocks – The hillocks along the way before the wood is entered are spoil-heaps from a small ironworks that operated in Hareshaw Dene from 1840 to 1848. It closed because of transport difficulties. The railway did not reach Bellingham until 1862.

Hareshaw Linn – At the Linn a small stream flows over a bed of limestone which overlies softer, more easily erodible shales. Undercutting, due to erosion, of the shales by the fall brings occasional collapses of the sandstone lip. So, in common with most falls, the gorge below it will gradually grow longer.

REFRESHMENTS:

There are pubs and cafés in Bellingham.

Walk 5   **WALLTOWN AND THIRLWALL CASTLE**   3m (4.8km)
Maps: OS Sheets Landranger 86; Pathfinder NY 66/76.
A pleasant walk along the line of Hadrian's Wall on the
Pennine Way.
Start: At 675662, Walltown Car Park.

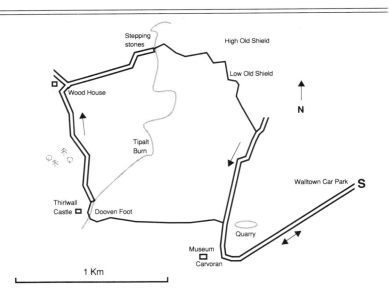

From the car park go westwards along the road to a junction opposite Carvoran
museum. Turn right for 200 yards, then cross a stile into a field on the left. Follow the
line of the wall and ditch along the Pennine Way. Cross the field to a stile and continue
downhill along the line of the fighting ditch, past ruinous Milecastle 46, to reach
some beeches. Cross a stile and descend to Tipalt Burn. Go through a gate at Holmhead
Guest House, cross Tipalt Burn on a footbridge and continue along the track past
Dooven Foot Cottage. Follow the track past **Thirlwall Castle** and farm yard, and take
the right fork uphill. Take the road to Tipalt Burn and cross it on stepping stones. Go
through a metal gate and along a sunken track towards Low Old Shield Farm. Cross
the farmyard and take the track around the front of the farmhouse. Continue uphill to
the High Old Shield road and on reaching a junction turn right. Continue over two

cattle grids back to Walltown Quarry and continue past the loading yard. Turn left at the buildings and return to the car park.

POINTS OF INTEREST:

Thirlwall Castle – The section of Hadrian's Wall near Thirlwall was one of its weakest points. The Scots pierced it at that point and 'thirled' it or 'threw it down' giving it the name Thirlwall. The castle was built sometime between 1306 and 1346 but the exact date is not known. Edward I is supposed to have slept there on 20th September 1306. The castle was built entirely of stones taken from the section of the Wall between Carvoran and Holmhead. In its heyday the de Thirlwalls lived there. Virtually impregnable, its walls were 9 feet thick, its windows very small and its dungeon in good repair. It was lived in until the 18th Century when Eleanora, the last heiress, married into the Swinburn family. They sold the castle to the Earl of Carlisle and it ceased to be inhabited.

Walk 6   **BERWICK RAMPARTS**   3m (4.8km)

Maps: OS Sheets Landranger 75; Pathfinder NT 95/NU 05.

A full circuit of the historic ramparts of by far the most interesting town in Northumberland.

Start: At 994534, Berwick railway station car park.

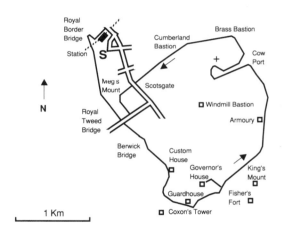

Go left to the main road and left again, over the railway bridge. At a junction go left for a few yards, and then left again through a small gate. Continue along a path through a park, with a splendid view of the castle, to reach the riverbank. Turn left, along a footpath which goes through the castle walls and under the Royal Border Bridge. Go under the Royal Tweed Bridge and along a cobbled street to reach a road. Cross and go down the flagged street ahead, soon passing the Custom House. Beyond, go down the first street on the left for a few yards to look at the Guardhouse with columns at its front. Walk to the ramparts and turn left, soon reaching Coxon's Tower, Fisher's Fort and the Crimean Gun. Continue along the ramparts and, just beyond the gun, turn left down a side street with a central lawn. At the end of the street turn left for a few yards to the Governor's House. Return to the ramparts and turn left, passing Kings Mount, then, on the left, a tall house fronted by lions and another, the Armoury, surrounded by a tall wall. Continue to Windmill Bastion, immediately beyond which turn right, along a street with a broad grassy area, to pass, on the left, the Barracks, now a museum. Near the end of the street go through a car park to visit Holy Trinity Parish Church. Go back to the ramparts and turn left, passing two more bastions, Brass and Cumberland. Stay on the ramparts, passing over the main street, Scotsgate, beyond which there is another bastion, Meg's Mount. Continue along the ramparts, passing a white stone statue of Annie, Lady Jerningham. Just short of the Royal Tweed Bridge climb some steps on the right to reach the main road and turn left. At the crossroads turn left and go along the road, going under Scotsgate. Continue along the left side of the road to Railway Street. Turn left back to the station car park.

POINTS OF INTEREST:

Before the end of the 13th century Berwick, which at that time had been part of Scotland for 300 years, had no defences of any significance. Following its capture by Edward I, a ditch, bank and wooden palisade were built, the palisade being replaced by a stone wall the following year. Between then and 1482, when the town became English for the last time, repair work only was carried out on the stone wall, despite the fact that during this period, when it was at the centre of the Border Troubles, Berwick changed hands on no less than 16 occasions. Between 1550 and 1557 a whole series of major works were carried out, and between 1558 and 1569, under Elizabeth I, still more defensive work was carried out, including the construction of the ramparts.

REFRESHMENTS:

Hotels, pubs and cafés in Berwick-on-Tweed.

Walk 7 **KEENLEY** 3m (4.8km)

Maps: OS Sheets Landranger 87; Pathfinder NY 85/95.

A very pleasant country ramble.

Start: At 822563, near Oakey Dene, on the Whitfield Road, 2 miles from Allendale.

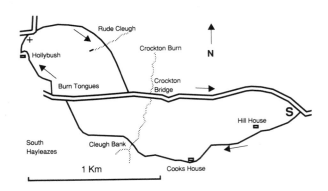

From the grass verge parking area go along a track on the south side of the road to a disused Hill House. Go between the buildings, uphill, alongside a holly hedge and ditch to reach a stile in a facing wall. Cross the field ahead, leaving it over a stile, and cross a farm road leading to High Oustley, on the right, aiming for Cooks House. Cross a stile in a facing wall and follow the path in front of the house. Go through a wicket and immediately turn right through a line of trees to go over a stile. Cross a private garden along a right of way. Now cross the field ahead, going downhill, and bearing left to reach a stile just before some trees. Cross, then go over a second stile and descend a bank to reach a footbridge over Cockton Burn. Climb a little way up the far bank to reach ruinous 'Cleugh Bank'. Here turn right to pass South Hayleazes, and continue diagonally left over three fields to cross a stile on to a road at Burn

Tongues. Cross the road, go through a kissing gate and cross a bridge. Go through a gate, turn left and continue to Holly Bush Farm. There, go through a gap in the corner of the wall on the right into a lane. Turn left, briefly, then go right through a gate, and cross a field to Keenley Methodist Chapel. Here turn right and go through Chapel House Wood. Turn right and follow a wall downhill into Rude Cleugh. Cross **Burnt Tongues Burn**; and reach a road by going over a stile. Turn left, along the road back to the starting point.

POINTS OF INTEREST:

Burnt Tongues Burn – There was once a corn mill at Burnt Tongues. It was built by William Hawdon in 1664 to break the monopoly of the Shield family, who owned Kingsmill and Newmill in Allendale.

Walks 8 & 9 WALLTOWN TO CAWFIELDS OR STEEL RIGG

3m (4.8km) or 5¹/₂m (8.8km)

Maps: OS Sheets Landranger 86; Pathfinder NY 66/76.

This superb walk includes some of the Nine Nicks of Thirlwall and the highest and most spectacular part of Hadrian's Wall .

Start: At 675662, Walltown car park.

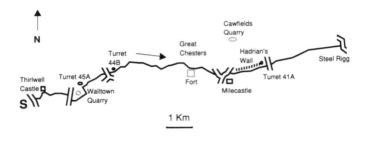

From the car park walk to the Wall at the top of the hill, turn right and walk eastwards across the Wall, passing behind Walltown Farm. Descend the steep slope from Milecastle 45 to Walltown Nick to reach a stile. Cross, and continue along a footpath, the Roman Military Way. Climb up to Muckleback Crag and follow the very clear Military Way to Great Chesters. From there stay on the course of the Pennine Way to reach Cawfields Picnic site, where the shorter walk finishes at the car park.

To derive the maximum advantage from your trip to the Wall do not go into the car park: instead, continue along the Wall as directed by the Pennine Way's acorn sign, passing Milecastle 42 to reach Caw Gap. Now climb the steep slope alongside the Wall and continue along it for 1¹/₂ miles. Turn left, briefly, where a road lies across your line of walk to reach Steel Rigg car park and the end of $5^1/_2$ miles of walking along the best part of Hadrian's Wall.

POINTS OF INTEREST:
From the summit of Winshields Crags the views are tremendous. To westward can be seen the Nine Nicks of Thirlwall and, beyond, the Solway. To the east, wave upon wave of Whin Sill dominates the view, while to the south are the Pennines, across the Tyne Valley. Westwards the view extends to Criffel in Kirkcudbrightshire.

REFRESHMENTS:
The Twice Brewed Inn on the B6318, Military Road (tel no: 0434 344534).

Walk 10   **WOOLER AND EARLE MILL**   3m (4.8km)

Maps: OS Sheets Landranger 75; Pathfinder NT 82/92.

An easy, level walk on the outskirts of Wooler.

Start: At 994279, at the south end of Wooler High Street.

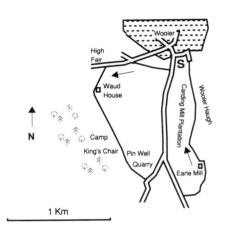

Go up Cheviot Street as far as the Youth Hostel and turn right along a footpath by the side of the hostel driveway. Follow it to the junction of Ramsey Lane and Common Road. Turn left along Common Road for a short distance and, just before **High Fair** is reached on the right, take the sloping track to a facing gate. The cottage on the left, Waud House, was built in 1772. Follow a clear path which goes straight down the valley, passing a grassy hillside on the left which, in early summer, is enamelled gold with the almond-scented flowers of gorse. The path also passes a crag, on the right, called the King's Chair. According to legend a king or a chieftain once sat on it to watch a battle. The nearby pool of water is fed by a spring called the Pin Well.

Cross a facing stile and walk to the road. Turn left and at the next junction turn right. Go southwards along the road to the first turning on the left, and go along that lane to reach Earle Mill. Annually from June to September, Meadow Cranesbill mottles the lane-side here with its big, blue flowers. Earle Mill is the site of an old corn mill which was twice burned down by the Scots, once in 1318 and again in the early 16th century. Go round the building and continue along the west side of the old mill-race. The stream on your right once served Earl Mill and the Carding, Dye and Wooler Mills. The water came from a weir across Wooler Water and was collected in a pond immediately above Earle Mill. The process of carding teases out clumps of wool fibre so that they run parallel to each other, ready for spinning. Small boards called wool cards are used. These have pieces of cloth, studded with little hooks. The clump of wool is spread over one card and the other is drawn across it until the wool is soft and fluffy. The carding mill, a three storey building, was destroyed by fire in the early 20th century.

Follow the path along the foot of the wooded slope on your left, cross a stile, go through a gate and walk ahead to reach a road. The red pantiled building across the road was once a dye mill. Wooler Mill, which dates from the 13th century, was still used as such in 1925. It is now a building store.

Turn left to return to the High Street.

POINTS OF INTEREST:
High Fair – Named after the Fair which was held there in Octobers during the late 19th century.

REFRESHMENTS:
Hotels, pubs and cafés in Wooler.

Walks 11 & 12   **HOLYSTONE AND LADY'S WELL**   3m (4.8km)
or $6^1/_2$m (10.4km)

Maps: OS Sheets Landranger 81; Pathfinder NT 80/90.
A pleasant, easy walk along flat agricultural land.
Start: At 956031, the roadside near the footbridge over the River
Coquet, on the Harbottle to Holystone road.

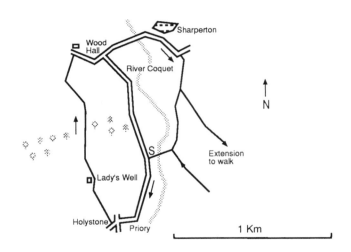

Go south, along the road, to **Holystone** village. Turn right, at the road junction and
continue through the village, going almost as far as the Salmon Inn car park. Now
take the signposted path to the Lady's Well. Go past the Well and through a gate on
the right to cross a field on a clear track, aiming for some trees beside a barn. Leave
the field through a gate and continue straight ahead to cross a stile. Follow the fence
on the left over the next field to reach the left side of some pine trees. Cross a stile
and, keeping close to the fence on the right, follow a grassy track for about 200 yards
to reach a gate on the right. Go through and continue along the track to a road. Turn
right to reach a T-junction. Continue straight ahead, soon crossing a bridge over the
River Coquet, skirting the hamlet of Sharperton on the left. Where the road takes a

sharp turn left, go through a gate in the fence on the right, descend to cross a ditch and climb the wooded bank ahead to reach a wicket. Now follow the fence on the right to reach a large footbridge over the River Coquet. Cross to return to the start.

A very fine, longer route can be followed if Walk 11 here and Walk 22 are continued. Follow this walk to a point just beyond Sharperton, then follow Walk 22 to reach the large footbridge over the River Coquet. Now follow this walk again to return to the start.

POINTS OF INTEREST:

Holystone – A priory of Augustinian nuns was founded at Holystone in the 12th century. The Prioress was among the nobles and clergy who paid homage to Edward I, Hammer of the Scots, at Berwick in 1296. By 1312 the Priory was poverty stricken and almost defenceless against Scottish raiders, and the nuns fled to Newcastle for a time in 1322. The Priory was dissolved in 1539.

REFRESHMENTS:

The Salmon Inn, Holystone (tel no: 0669 50285).

Walk 13   FEATHERSTONE AND LAMBLEY FARM   3m (5.6km)

Maps: OS Sheets Landranger 86; Pathfinder NY 66/76 and NY 65/75.

A riverside and woodland walk, offering a variety of birds and plant life.

Start: At 673613, Featherstone footbridge over the South Tyne.

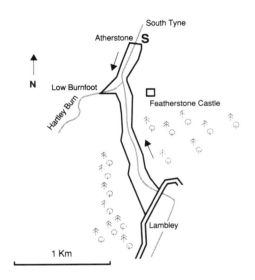

Cross the footbridge and turn left along a riverside path from which **Featherstone Castle** is clearly seen on the other side of the river. The path bears away from the river and crosses meadowland towards Low Burnfoot Farm. Cross Hartley Bun on a metal footbridge, turn sharp left and follow the burn side to open fields. Turn right into a field and follow waymarkers to a stile near a hawthorn hedge. Follow the path through two gates, and on reaching Lambley Farm turn left on to a road bridge. Cross and turn left, through a gate, to reach a path running parallel to the river. Follow this, passing Featherstone Castle, to reach the start of the walk.

POINTS OF INTEREST:
Featherstone Castle – Perhaps one of the most attractive of all the border strongholds. It is said to be haunted by a ghostly bridal party. The oldest part of the castle is 13th century, though it was restored in the 14th century. When peace began to settle over the Borders following the Union of the Crowns in 1603 extensive reconstruction work took place.

Northumberland is filled with legends and ghost stories, as a result, perhaps, of its being much battered by warfare and having a thinly scattered population. With little education and entertainment available, a rich folklore was handed down by word of mouth over generations during the long dark winters. And Northumbrians can still tell a good tale, and the taller the better.

Walk 14 **THE HARTHOPE VALLEY AND COLD LAW** 3m (4.8km)
Maps: OS Sheets Landranger 75; Pathfinder NT 82/92.
A grand little walk, with easy climbing to the summit of Cold Law.
Start: At 955227, on the Harthope Valley road.

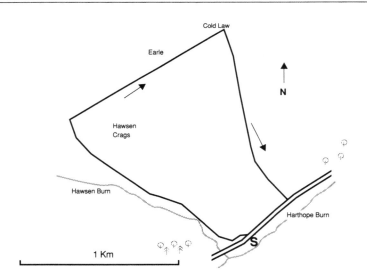

From the roadside, grassy parking area on the left of the road about $^1/_2$ mile beyond Langlee cottage go up the valley for 50 yards to reach a path signposted 'To Broadstruther', leading off to the right. After 300 yards the path levels: just before it descends to a sheepfold take a narrow path, right, above the sheepfold. Continue in the same direction, crossing several paths, following Hawsen Burn, on your left, upstream.

Cross a sike and 200 yards beyond it, where the path bifurcates, take the right fork, uphill. Follow this clear path which levels after $^1/_3$ mile and reaches a fence. This is a poorly drained area where rushes abound and sphagnum mosses and bright green polytrichum flourish. Turn right and follow the fence, on your left, up **Cold Law** as far as a large rock. At the rock bear right, away from the fence, to reach a trig point after

36

100 yards. From the trig point continue south, with Cheviot on your right, to reach a large cairn. There, bear right past an outcrop and keep ahead, following a line of cairns to reach a good track. On the way you are sure to see some *corby*, as carrion crows are known locally. With their scavenging ways they are the dustmen of the countryside, eating all dead creatures as well as catching insects. During the autumn and early winter the corby varies its diet, adding mice, voles and other small mammals to the menu. Turn left, downhill, along the track and, where it bifurcates, keep right on a good path back to the road and the start of the walk.

POINTS OF INTEREST:

Cold Law – The trig (triangulation) point on Cold Law was built by the Ordnance Survey to enable them to map the country accurately. The Survey depends on using three known points (hence triangulation) all of which are visible from each other. The original Ordnance Survey was prepared for military purposes and a key point at that time was established on Cheviot summit in the early 1800's. The present one is supported on an 11ft long pile driven through the peat to the solid ground below.

Walk 15   **HIGH HUMBLETON**   3m (4.8km)

Maps: OS Sheets Landranger 75; Pathfinder NT 82/92.

A gentle climb along a good path with wide views; and a descent along the lower slopes of historic Humbleton Hill.

Start: At 974284, at the south end of High Humbleton.

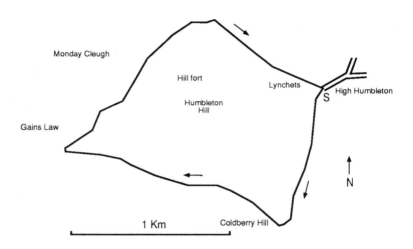

From the parking space at the end of the surfaced road, go along a lane and up a slope for almost $^1/_4$ mile to reach a gate to the left of a ruinous cottage called Drythropple. A few yards past the gate take the right fork and follow the path hill. Humbleton Hill, on your right, was once capped by a pre-historic hill fort and the summit is still partially encircled by the walls of a stout rampart which was built to protect a citadel-like enclosure. The fort is one of many similar hill forts scattered across the Cheviots. It was in use up to, and possibly beyond, the Roman occupation.

Follow the path through a gap in a wall, continue ahead for a few hundred yards and turn right at a small cairn. Soon a clear path comes into view: take this, going downhill, along the lower slopes of Humbleton Hill. Near the foot of the hill the path turns right and follows a wall on the left, passing a pond, also on the left.

Just past the pond, and to the right of the path, there are strip lynchets, cultivation terraces, running parallel to your line of walk. Throughout England there are many examples of this Anglo-Saxon or medieval farming method. In Northumberland, however, some lynchets on poor land, such as these, date from as late as 19th century. Just past the lynchets, go through a gate to rejoin the lane at High Humbleton, so completing the walk.

POINTS OF INTEREST:

Monday Cleugh, the ravine to the left as you descend the lower slopes of Humbleton Hill, is a dry valley, a sub-glacial water course eroded by meltwater flowing under pressure beneath the ice at the end of the last Ice Age.

On the 13th September 1402, this area was the scene of a battle between the Scots under Douglas and the Earl of Northumberland and his son Harry Hotspur with a force of English archers. The English won the day. News of this battle forms the start of Shakespeare's play 'Henry IV'.

Walk 16 BIDDLESTONE TOWNFOOT AND SINGMOOR $3\frac{1}{2}$m (5.6km)

Maps: OS Sheets Landranger 75; Pathfinder NT 80/90.

A lovely walk if you want to be alone among the heather.

Start: At 961083, the T-junction at Biddlestone.

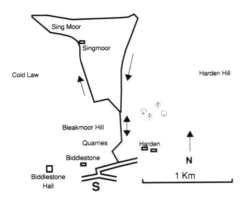

Take the road going uphill from the T-junction for 30 yards towards a **quarry** and turn right along a road signposted 'Biddlestone Town Foot'. After 300 yards go through the first gate seen along the road's left side. Cross a field to a wicket at its highest point and immediately go left, through a gate on to a track. Turn right, uphill, and keep right at a fork. Go through a gate and along the track ahead which curves left and, in $\frac{1}{4}$ mile, passes a sheepfold on the right. Stay on the track as it dips and goes through a gate, and then continues past Singmoor cottage and through another gate. Shepherds no longer live in isolated cottages like Singmoor because the facilities are, at best, primitive and there are no nearby schools for their children. These days, when he makes his morning and late afternoon inspections of his flock, the shepherd does so either on horseback, in a Landrover or on a scrambler bike.

Go to the left of a small plantation to reach its corner. From there take a faint path, uphill and curving slightly left, and stay with it for about $1/4$ mile. Where it bends slightly right a track coming in from the left is passed: stay on the original path for a further 200 yards to reach a cairn some 100 yards short of a gate. Turn sharp right, following cairns across the moor, and descend past the top of Singmoor Plantation on your right. Now go slightly left, with Hazleton Rig Burn in the dip on your left. When a gate at the right-hand corner of a plantation is reached do not go through it: instead turn sharp right along a path for 500 yards. On reaching some sheep pens, go through a gate on their left, follow the track into a dip, and then go up to a right-hand gate. Follow a track beside a fence on the left and after 300 yards bear right to rejoin the Singmoor track. From there retrace your steps to the start.

POINTS OF INTEREST:

Quarry – The red felsite being quarried at Harden was formed some 300 million years ago. Harden felsite has been used to surface many roads and was used in London to make a 'red carpet' road along the mall to Buckingham Palace.

Walk 17   WEST ALLEN AND MOHOPE   3¹/₂m (5.6km)

Maps: OS Sheets Landranger 87; Pathfinder NY 65/75.

A pleasant walk through a former lead mining area.

Start: At 783516, a stile in a wall just beyond Bates Hill, opposite
Farneyside Cottages.

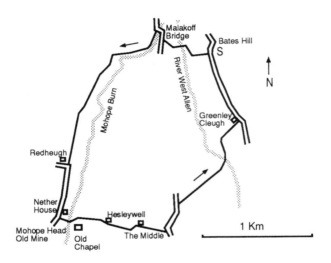

From the stile go downhill, left of the gully, cross a footbridge over the River West
Allen and turn left along the field boundary. Go diagonally right to a field gate on to
a road above Malakoff Bridge. Turn right, over the bridge, and, after 20 yards, turn
left through a gate into a field. Cross diagonally left to another gate. Go through and
continue with the river on your left. Where it bends sharp left, cross a small feeder,
Blind Burn, turn right up a grassy bank and go through a gate in a stone wall. Continue
in the same direction, along the ridge, exiting through a field gate. Now aim for two
cottages ahead. Go through a gate into the yard of the left-hand one and on to a
surfaced road. Turn left, passing Mohope Chapel on your right, and continue to Nether
House on your left. In the angle of the wall on your left, where the road bends sharp
right beyond the buildings, there is a stone stile. Cross this, and immediately turn left

along a wall to cross the Mohope and Wellhope Burns on footbridges. Continue diagonally up the bank along a clear track, go through a wicket and, skirting the left side of a meadow, aim for an old railway wagon shed left of Hesleywell Farm. Go through a gate, leaving the large shed on your left, turn right on to the road and go straight ahead over a wall stile. Cross the field ahead, going uphill to reach a stile about 30 yards to the left of a building. Cross and continue along a lane. Turn left, go through a gate and aim for the building ahead, The Middle, and a little to your left. Go through a gate into a yard, leaving over a stile in the wall in front of the house. Continue along the edge of a field and go through a wicket. Continue towards a gate about 3 yards to the right of Broadlea farmhouse. Cross a wall stile to the left of this gate. Turn left, along the road, for 250 yards to reach a row of trees on the right. Go through a gate and continue to the left of these trees, cross a facing wall by a stile and continuing along the wall on your right. Go through a gateway in a wire fence and along a muddy track to the river. Cross a footbridge and continue below the treeline, parallel to the river on your left, going through a wicket and over a feeder. Bear right, along an old track which zig-zags uphill and goes through a gate. Climb to another field gate and continue along the right edge of a meadow, aiming for the right side of a farmhouse, Greenley Cleugh. Cross a stile on to a road. Turn left for $^1/_2$ mile back to the start.

Note: Please avoid old levels. Take care when exploring the area. Some shafts may be invisible so it is recommended that you keep to the paths.

Walk 18   **CAWFIELDS AND HALLPEAT MOSS** $3^1/_2$m (5.6km)
Maps: OS Sheets Landranger 87; Pathfinder NY 66/76.
*Upland grazing on the outward journey and a return along the
Wall ridge.*
Start: At 714665, Cawfields picnic site car park.

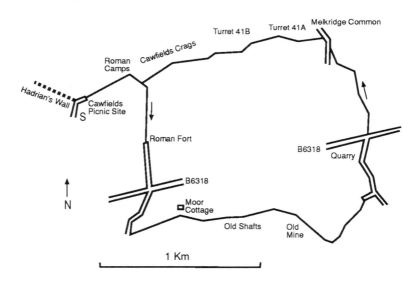

From the car park take the footpath along the edge of quarry lake. Go through the line
of the Wall at a kissing gate and, ignoring the Pennine Way sign, bear right to a clear
track that crosses the vallum to a surfaced road. Cross the B6318, the Military Road at
Milecastle Inn and uphill southwards. About 100 yards past a house on the left, go
right, over a ladder stile, into a field and along a footpath signposted 'Hallpeat Moss'.
Where the path is indistinct bear south east towards crags and limekilns. Go through
a wicket towards some well preserved limekilns, beyond which bear left and cross a
wall at a stile. Go diagonally across the field corner to reach a stile near a gate and
continue uphill to a farmhouse. Turn right along the edge of a field, exiting on to a
road. Turn left to reach the Military Road. Cross, go over a stile and take a farm track
northwards, past **Shield on the Wall**. At the end of the wall on your left, go diagonally

44

left cross the vallum, following waymarkers. Go round the end of a ridge and cross a ladder stile on to the road at Caw Gap. Turn right, along the road for 50 yards to a sign, 'Milecastle 42'. Go though a wicket on the left, then bear right to reach the Pennine Way on the line of the Wall. Follow the line of the Wall to Milecastle 42, and return to the car park via a wicket.

POINTS OF INTEREST:
Shield on the Wall – The name 'Shield' at the farm is a clear pointer that this was one of the summer grazing grounds. While cattle grazed these grounds the family lived in the shielings or huts.

REFRESHMENTS:
The Milecastle Inn (tel no: 0434 320682) on the B6318.

Walk 19   **VINDOLANDA AND HENSHAW** $3^1/_2$m (5.6km)
Maps: OS Sheets Landranger 87; Pathfinder NY 66/76.
A route that goes through the grounds of Vindolanda Museum.
Start: At 768665, Vindolanda car park.

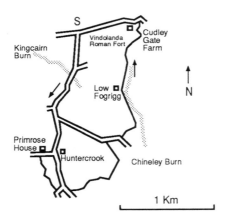

From the car park's main exit go left for 100 yards, and turn left through a gate at a
fingerpost. Walk south across a field to reach a gate into a lane. Go up Kingcairn Hill.
On reaching a surfaced road continue southward along it. Where it bends left, go
straight ahead, as indicated by a road sign, to Henshaw. At Huntercrook, turn right
past Brownside House. Just beyond Primrose House turn left, through a metal gate, to
Henshaw Hall. Go round the house and over a stile in a wall. Go across the field
ahead, staying close to the field boundary on your left, to reach a stile. Go over, walk
to another stile and at the far end of the next field enter Henshaw village. Go past two
chapels to reach a road junction. Cross to a wicket at the back of another chapel, now
the W I Hall. Take the footpath along the edge of a field, continuing through four
more wickets to reach a farm road. Cross to enter another field through another wicket.
Climb the left side of the hill ahead, go through a gate and cross a stile at Parkside

46

Farm. Follow a track to the right of farm buildings, exiting through a gate. Now climb a field path to reach another gate. Turn right, along a road, for 200 yards. Leave the road at a left bend, going over a stile into a field. Follow a cart track diagonally across the field, aiming for a pylon. Head due north, going above Chineley Burn. Cross a bridge over Bean Burn just before it enters Chineley Burn at Low Fogrigg and follow a path to the terrace above. Go through a wicket and follow a path to a stile in a fence. Continue to reach the museum boundary fence which is crossed over a stile. Turn right along a waymarked path, following the burn. Cross a white bridge and go round the side of the museum grounds to reach Stalemate. Leave **Vindolanda** through a wicket and turn left, past Cudley Gate Farm, to go back to the car park.

POINTS OF INTEREST:
Vindolanda – The fort probably dates to the early 80's AD. It was rebuilt several times before being abandoned finally in the late 4th century.

Walk 20   **HAYDON BRIDGE AND ELRINGTON**   3¹/₂m (5.6km)

Maps: OS Sheets Landranger 87; Pathfinder NY 86/96.

A nice, all seasons field and woodland walk.

Start: At 843639, the parking bay on the cemetery side of the road at Haydon Bridge.

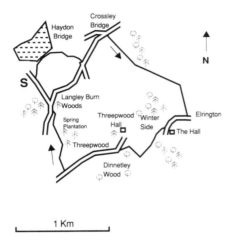

From the parking bay, cross the road to a stile. Cross and go diagonally towards the school. Go right at a wall, below some trees, and continue to a lane. Follow the lane past the school and some terraced houses to reach a wood, entering it over a footbridge. Follow a path that climbs out of the wood and goes between a field on the left and a deep gorge on the right. At the end of the path turn left on to the A686. Cross and go down the road's right side to the junction with the A69. Now cross a stile at a field gate on the right. Go over two fields and in the third one cross a stile at its left side into Elrington Wood. Cross Crossley Burn on a footbridge and follow a path uphill, with a wall on the left. Where the wall ends there are several paths, so follow the waymarkers and go straight ahead to reach a stile beside a gate near some blackthorn bushes. Cross it into a field and follow the path close to a dry stone wall on the right. Next, follow a dyke on the left, heading towards **Elrington**. There, turn right on to a farm track and take it along the top of a pasture, passing through a gate at a stone bridge across Elrington Burn. Do not go through the next gate: instead, take the left fork to Dinnetley, a very clear farm track without which Dinnetley would be accessible only on foot or horseback. The waymarked track follows the garden wall on the right and then descends to reach Dinnetley Wood through a waymarked wicket. Turn left and follow a path to a plank bridge over Threepwood Burn. Continue uphill, and leave the wood at a road, from where Threepwood Hall can be seen. Turn left, along the road until the walls on each side recess for gates. Just before the signpost on the right, turn right over a stone stile and cross a field to some larches. From these, follow waymarkers diagonally downhill to reach a kissing gate into Spring Plantation. Leave over a stile and go down the field ahead to reach a wall stile. Go over into Langley Burn Woods. Go through the wood, turn right on the A686 and then go left, back to the start.

POINTS OF INTEREST:
Elrington – once a large village, and one of the 12 towns of Tynedale.

REFRESHMENTS:
Available in Haydon Bridge.

Walk 21   SINDERHOPE AND ACTON $3\frac{1}{2}$m (5.6km)

Maps: OS Sheets Landranger 87; Pathfinder NY 85/95.

A lovely, easy walk in the secluded dale of the River East Allen, a former lead mining area.

Start: Car Park, on the B6295. Sinderhope Centre.

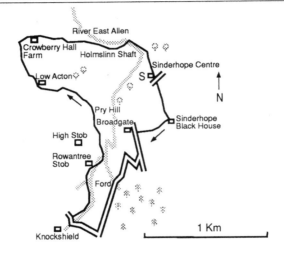

Because some of the old shaft-caps have become dangerous, you are advised to keep to the paths on this walk.

From the car park cross the road, go through a gate and over the field ahead to a ruin called Black House. Turn right and continue past the rear of High Sinderhope Farm and Parlour Close Cottage. Cross a stile and turn downhill towards Broadgate Farm Riding Centre. Turn left, along a road for 100 yards, then fork right along a road to cross the River East Allen. Continue along the road and take the first turn on the right. Go along this road, soon crossing Knockshield Burn, and turn right at a signpost to cross the field behind Knockburn Farm, following markers. Cross the wooden stiles ahead, bridge Hole Sike and go to the right of ruinous Rowantree Stob. Cross Knockshield Burn and continue close to the hedge and the burn on your left, for about

200 yards to re-cross Knockshield Burn. Take a short, steep climb, up a fairly wet hill. There is no clear path to follow, but there are stiles all the way to Pry Hill. Continue to reach a road. Cross and go over the field ahead to reach a stile. Go downhill, bearing slightly left to reach Acton Burn, which is crossed on a footbridge. Now go left, contouring to Low Acton Farm and continue by following waymarkers towards Crowberry Hall Farm. Go between the farmhouse and some outbuildings and over the Crowberry footbridge to reach a crossing of paths, at a signpost. Go straight ahead to Holmslinn Waterfall and continue over the River East Allen on the new county bridge. Turn right along the riverside, on your right, to reach and cross the Acton road. Now climb uphill back to the Sinderhope Centre.

Walk 22   **HEPPLE AND COQUETDALE** $3^1/_2$m (5.6km)

Maps: OS Sheets Landranger 81; Pathfinder NT 80/90.

*The going is mostly flat, except when passing High and Low
Farnham, and the views are good.*

Start: At 982003, a lay-by on the north side of Hepple Bridge.

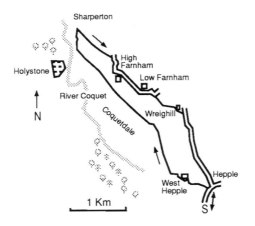

Walk north towards Hepple and after $^1/_4$ mile turn left along a road signposted West
Hepple to reach West Hepple Farm. Go to the right of the farm buildings and leave
the farmyard by going right, briefly, and then turning left along a track. Just past some
sheds, go right, through a gate, and follow a track that soon goes left to reach a gate.
Go through and turn right. Continue through fields as directed by yellow marks on the
gateposts, going downhill all the way. Then, as the path begins to climb, turn left,
close to the fence on your left, for 100 yards to reach a plantation. Turn right alongside
it. Turn left, briefly, over a bridge then go right, close to the fence on your right for
just over $^1/_2$ mile to reach a long, white footbridge. Do not cross: instead, follow the
fence, on the left to reach a wicket. Do not go through: instead turn right and go
across the hillside, passing two stone gateposts to reach a stile. Cross to reach the

52

lower right-hand corner of a plantation. Continue with the plantation on your left, then go along a second plantation and through a gate on to a road. Turn right and pass **High Farnham** and Low Farnham Farms. Where, 200 yards past Low Farnham, the road turns sharp left, follow the track ahead to **Wreighill**. Go to the right of it, past a barn on the right, cross a cattle grid and continue to a gate where the track bifurcates. Here go right, along a track that dips, rises and dips again to reach another bifurcation just before a gate. Go straight ahead, through the gate, and on to Hepple. Turn right along the road and retrace your steps to the lay-by.

POINTS OF INTEREST:

High Farnham – A circular, stone-lined well in the trees to the north of High Farnham is all that remains of a pele tower that was burned by 50 men of Teviotdale in 1546.

Wreighill – Pronounced 'Wreehill' this means 'felons' or gallow's hill. A beacon on the hill behind the cottages was used to summon aid. In 1412 the raiding Scots wiped out the hamlet, but it was re-established, only to be decimated again in 1665 when almost all the inhabitants died of the plague. In 1816 twenty people were living at Wreighill, but today it is shrouded in obscurity.

Walk 23   **ALLENDALE AND SCOTCH HALLS** $3^1/_2$m (5.6km)

Maps: OS Sheets Landranger 87; Pathfinder NY 85/95.

From this walk there are good views over Allendale Town and along the Allen Valley.

Start: At 839559, the steps beside Isaac's Well, Allendale Town.

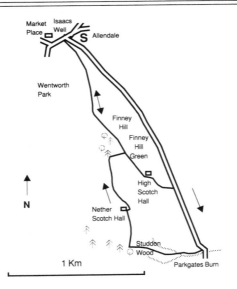

From the steps go through the Allenfields housing estate and continue diagonally right across the field ahead to cross a stone stile midway along a facing wall. Continue to a stile between two trees growing close together. Go over and immediately turn right, across the field ahead to a gateway. On the left of the next field climb a stone stile and continue uphill towards a wood, going through an iron gate. Keep alongside the wood, then bear right, briefly, to look for a stone stile in the opposite wall. Cross on to a farm track which goes in front of Finney Hill Green. Beyond, go through a facing stile at a gate. Cross the next field to High Scotch Hall. Go over a stile halfway along the wall, turn left and go through a gate on to a farm drive in front of the house. Go along the drive to reach a country road and turn right along it. At a sharp bend, follow a path through a lovely wood. The path joins the B6295. Do not cross the road:

54

instead, go right, briefly, to a seat and go over a stile behind it. Cross a stream on a plank bridge and climb the bank. Go left towards Nether Scotch Hall, crossing a stile on to the drive. Follow yellow markers to reach some trees, and continue northwards over three fields. On reaching a copse, turn into a track through a gate at the back of Finney Hill Green and go along it to rejoin the path used on the outward leg. Retrace your steps to **Isaac's Well**.

POINTS OF INTEREST:
Isaac's Well – The Well was the first fresh water supply to the village of Allendale Town in 1849. An obelisk in the churchyard is built to the memory of Isaac Holden, a philanthropist who travelled the dales on horseback, selling tea.

REFRESHMENTS:
There are tearooms in Allendale.

Walk 24   **BLANCHLAND AND PENNYPIE** $3^1/_2$m (5.6km)
Maps: OS Sheets Landranger 87; Pathfinder NY 85/95 and
NY 84/94.

*A walk from picturesque Blanchland with good views of the North
Pennines.*

Start: At 962505, Blanchland car park.

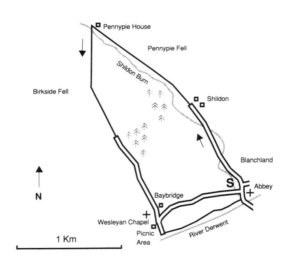

From Blanchland car park go left, along a surfaced road marked 'No Through Road',
and with Shildon Burn on your left. After about $^1/_2$ mile climb a short, steep hill and,
still on the road, continue below the hillside hamlet of Shildon. Ruinous Shildon
Smelt Mill is in Shildon Plantation, opposite the hamlet. It was one of Northumberland's
oldest lead mines, opening in 1475 and closing in 1860. A Forestry Commission
notice advises – 'Please stay out of these woods, they contain old mine shafts which
are dangerous'. Past the hamlet continue along the road, now a stony, enclosed track,
for $^1/_2$ mile passing, on your left, lots of Sitka Spruce and Scots Pine, all stood to
attention in serried lines. As the track climbs steadily between pastures, and with
Shildon Beck still below and on your left, a large barn is passed, on the right. When

the track curves right to **Pennypie House**, a working farm, 1,150 feet above sea level, continue straight ahead, through a facing gate on to Bulbeck Common. Turn left, and either bridge or ford the infant Shildon Burn. Now follow a clear track across the moor with a stone wall on your left. This is an old drove road and heads southwards. Soon a step stile is reached: cross it and continue over Birkside Fell. At the end of the moor go through a gate and continue along a steeply descending lane into Baybridge hamlet in the Derwent Valley. Turn right, at the road junction and go along the road to where, just past Baybridge picnic area, but before a three arched bridge, turn left along a signposted riverside path back into Blanchland.

POINTS OF INTEREST:
Pennypie House – So named because this one-time ale house sold penny pies to miners who passed there, taking lead ore to the Carrier's Way.

REFRESHMENTS:
The Lord Crewe Arms Hotel, Blanchland (tel no: 0434 675251).

Walks 25 & 26   ROTHBURY TO PAUPERHAUGH BRIDGE

4m (6.4km) or 13³/₄m (22km)

Maps: OS Sheets Landranger 81; Pathfinder NU 00/10.

A section of the long river walk from Rothbury to Felton.

Start: At 058016, the Coquet bridge in Rothbury.

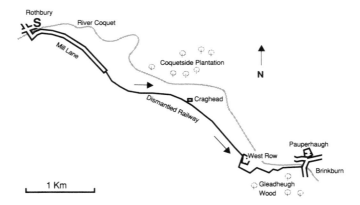

From the north side of the bridge cross the Coquet and turn left along the Hexham road, the B6342, for ¹/₄ mile. Now take the left-hand road, marked 'No Through Road', to a point just short of a bridge, and go left on the road under the bridge. After 100 yards, where the road bends left to Wagtail Farm, keep ahead, going through a gate and along a track. Go through another gate and continue to reach a railway cutting after ¹/₂ mile. Go through a gate and, after 50 yards, turn left into a field. Cross this and pass to the right of Crag Head cottage going through a gate. Now take the track across six fields to reach West Row farm. Turn right through a gate at the farm buildings to reach a T-junction. Go right to a road junction. Go through a gate on the left, cross a field and, just past a cottage, go through the right-hand of two gates and continue alongside the fence on your left for 100 yards to reach another gate, also on the left.

Turn left, then turn right alongside, firstly, a fence, then a hedge, on the right. Just before the end of a field bear left for 100 yards and go through a wicket. Go through a plantation to reach another wicket. Continue alongside a sike, cross a bridge and go left, around a field above the Coquet to reach a gate. Cross the field ahead to reach a gate near Pauperhaugh Bridge.

This walk is the first section of a walk along the River Coquet. The second section is described in Walk 90. The very best walk, however, is to complete the two sections as one long walk.

Walk 27   **HOLY ISLAND AND EMANUEL HEAD**   4m (6.4km)
Maps: OS Sheets Landranger 75; Pathfinder NU 04/14.
A circuit of the eastern end of the island.
Start: At 128421, the main car park in Holy Island village.

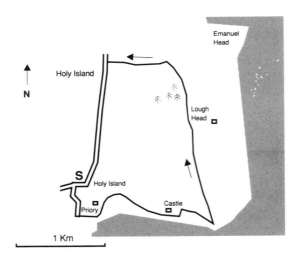

From the car park turn right, then left on to the main road. At the end of it the road
turns right, and immediately left to the market place. Beyond the cross, follow the
notice to **Lindisfarne Priory**, go to the tower side of the church and on to a gateway
in the stone wall on the right. Go through, turn left and follow a winding track to a
grassy shelf. Turn left up a stony path to the top of the ridge. Continue along it to the
right of a coastguard building. Go past a storm beacon and descend to a black-tarred
fishery shed. Go along a grassy track, bearing right around the Ouse to join the road
going eastwards from the village. Bear right towards the castle, go through a gate at
the road end and continue towards the castle, following a path to the right of it. Bear
right at the next outcrop of dolerite and cross a grassy area to reach a fenced area of
lime kilns. Bear right to Castle Point at the south-east tip of the island. Go left along
the coast, following a grassy ridge above a clay cliff for about 250 yards. Now go left

and follow the path below the fence line. Cross a stile just beyond a marshy area and bear left along an old wagonway for 200 yards. Go through a wicket and after another 100 yards look for a wide grassy path crossing the wagonway. Turn left and take the path bearing right along the edge of the dunes to the right. This leads to a junction with a wide lane, Straight Lonnen. Turn left, along it, southwards, past the junction with Crooked Lonnen to return to the car park.

POINTS OF INTEREST:

Lindisfarne Priory – The first priory, a modest wooden structure, was built by St Aidan who arrived from Iona in 635. While he was away converting the Celts his monks stayed on the island developing a tradition for outstanding art and learning. Soon their influence spread beyond Northumbria and for a while all Europe looked towards this tiny centre of civilisation. In 875 the Vikings fired the priory. The monks had just enough time to collect their precious relics, mostly the bones of Saints, and flee to the mainland. They never returned; and it was not until 1093 that a stone priory and church were built.

REFRESHMENTS:
Available in Holy Island village.

Walk 28   SILLYWREA AND HARSONDALE   4m (6.4km)

Maps: OS Sheets Landranger 87; Pathfinder NY 66/76 and NY 86/96.

A woodland and riverside walk of rare beauty.

Start: At 796643, the privately owned Plankey Mill car park.

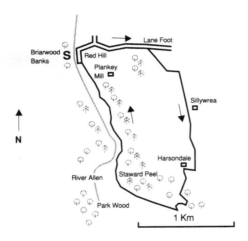

Leave the car park by walking round the back of some old buildings and on to the road. Go uphill to Lane Foot on the left. Just past the house, cross a stile on the right, alongside Linn Burn, and follow the field edge to Sillywrea Farm. On reaching the farm turn right along a farm road, passing an arched stone building and going through a metal gate on the left. Go uphill, with a wall on your right, aiming for a stile at the top. Cross and turn right along the field edge to reach a gate. Continue past an old cottage and some beech trees. Cross a step stile on the right and go past a line of hawthorns to reach a corner. Cross a wall by way of a stile on the left. Descend a field to reach a stile next to a gate. Cross on to Harsondale Farm road. Go down it towards the farm, and just before some farm buildings turn left over a stile. Follow the hedge line down the field and go through a wicket into a wood. Continue downhill, going through the wood and crossing a footbridge. Climb up the other side and follow the footpath to the top of the slope. Cross a stile into a meadow and cross diagonally right to reach a stile. Cross to go back into the wood. Follow a path which crosses a ridge with drops on either side. Beyond ruinous Staward, follow a steep, winding path downhill to reach a stone wall at the bottom. Turn right, following the course of Harsondale Burn, and cross it on a footbridge. Follow the footpath towards the **River Allen** and walk along its bank. Leave the wood into a meadow, with Plankey Farm at the far end, and continue along the river to a stile. Cross and take the path between the river and a fence, passing a suspension bridge, to reach the road and the car park where it all began. To the left, across the river, on this final section of the walk are **Briarwood Banks**.

POINTS OF INTEREST:
River Allen – The Allen banks provide excellent walks with a variety of plants, trees and wildlife.
Briarwood Banks – One of the Northumberland Wildlife Trust's nature reserves.

Walk 29   **FOURSTONES AND BRIDGE END**   4m (6.4km)
Maps: OS Sheets Landranger 87; Pathfinder NY 86/96.
An easy walk along the South Tyne to its confluence with the North Tyne.
Start: At 888679, Fourstones village, opposite St Aidan's Church.

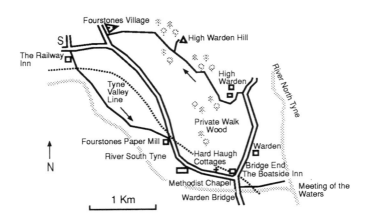

Go 'doon the bank', past the Railway Inn and cross the Tyne Valley Railway. Pass Riverside Cottage on the left, turning left along a footpath to reach the South Tyne. Follow the riverside path for $^1/_2$ mile and, where it bifurcates, go left, through a kissing gate, and continue along a wet path over rough pasture, rejoining the river through a corner gate. Keep along the riverside path for $^1/_2$ mile to reach **Fourstones Paper Mill**. Turn right past it, and follow the road past Hard Haugh Cottages. A little further on, pass Warden Methodist Chapel to reach Bridge End. Turn right, briefly, then left, before Warden Bridge, as directed by a footpath sign for 'Meeting of the Waters'. Go along the riverside path to reach, after $^1/_2$ mile, the confluence of the rivers North and South Tyne. Retrace your steps to Warden Bridge and turn right, along the road, to Warden, where the **church** is well worth a visit. From the church, retrace your steps briefly, and turn right, along the road, for $^1/_2$ mile. Turn left at a bridleway sign, 'Fourstones $1^1/_2$m', cross a cattle grid and follow the main drive which curves uphill to reach High Warden estate cottages. Continue past them, and just beyond Swaindale Cottage on your left, go along a cart track to reach the edge of Private Walk Wood. Turn right along the wood's edge to join a broad cart track through a metal gate. Follow the track to the top of a field and go through a gate. Turn left, beside some trees, along the field edge, exiting through a gate. Go diagonally right up the next pasture, to cross a corner wall.

From here there is an interesting diversion. Turn right, alongside the wall, to reach the trig point at the top of **High Warden Hill**. Retrace your steps, turn right and continue close to the wall on the left. Turn left, through a gate, into Laverick Plantation and follow a clear woodland path to meet a bridle track coming up from the left. Go along the bridle track with the plantation on your right. Beyond the plantation the track curves left, past a cottage on the right, continuing through a gate and down the edge of a field. Turn left, through a metal gate, then go right, along a gated cart track and through a farmyard, back to Fourstones.

POINTS OF INTEREST:

Fourstones Paper Mill – The mill, founded in 1763, is one of the oldest paper mills in the country.

Warden Church – The church of St Michael and All Angels was founded in AD 704 and has the oldest Saxon tower in Northumberland.

High Warden Hill – Locally known as 'Watch Hill' because from its top, the North and South Tyne valleys can be seen, as can all of Hexhamshire and much of Tynedale. It is also occasionally known as 'Camp Hill' because of the ancient earthwork on its summit.

REFRESHMENTS:

The Railway Inn, Fourstones (tel no: 0434 674279).
The Boatside Inn, Bridge End (tel no: 0434 602233).

Walk 30   **BAMBURGH AND BUDLE POINT**   4m (6.4km)
Maps: OS Sheets Landranger 75; Pathfinder NU 13/23.
*Dunes, whinstone crags, rich arable fields, an historic village
and a superb castle.*
Start: At 18349, the main car park, opposite Bamburgh Castle.

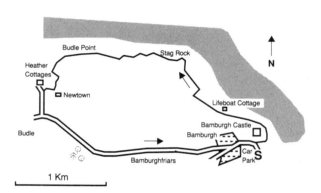

From the car park cross the road and follow a path to the right of **Bamburgh Castle**.
Continue to the front of it and take the narrow path that descends to the right of a
wooden fence just across the surfaced road from the castle entrance. Follow the line
of the fence at the foot of the bank, bearing left and aiming for the north corner of the
castle rock. The path turns left after passing beneath a cliff and, after passing some
castle ruins to the left, it bears right to join a road at Lifeboat Cottage. Go right, cross
Mill Burn and climb to the top of the next hill. Turn right, and cross the dunes to the
high water mark. Turn left and continue towards Harkness Rocks. If the tide is out,
walk along the rocks below a grassy bank. If the sea is rough climb the bank and
continue along the roadside to the lighthouse. Go to the left of the lighthouse and
along a path at the base of a grassy bank above the rocks, that leads to a sandy bay. Go

along the shore as far as the lifebuoy, and take the path to the left there, going up the bank and bearing right along the edge of a golf course. The path goes through the remains of a wall and leads to the start of a wide stony path. Follow this north-west, around Budle Point. Go left, round the gun emplacement, then go sharp left on to the golf links. Continue to the right of the greens, then go right, beside a wide track, to reach a gateway. Go through on to a surfaced road. Bear left along the road to a gate. Turn left through it and go uphill to another gate. Go through on to the main road. Turn left and continue over the brow of the hill and along the road verge towards Bamburgh, reaching the village centre. From there return to the car park.

POINTS OF INTEREST:

Bamburgh Castle – Sitting large and square on its dolerite foundations the castle began as a fortification built by Ida, first of the Northumbrian Kings, in 547. It was called Dinguraroy and was surrounded by a hedge. The castle became the centrepiece of a sizeable kingdom. Later, Ida's grandson, Ethelfrith, gave it to his Queen, Bebba, and it became 'Bebbanburgh' in the 7th century. After that it was linked with some of the most significant events in English history.

REFRESHMENTS:

Numerous available in Bamburgh.

Walk 31   **ALNMOUTH AND LESBURY**   4m (6.4km)
Maps: OS Sheets Landranger 81; Pathfinder NU 21/22.
A close look at mud flats, almost unique in Northumberland.
Start: At 250107, Alnmouth Common car park.

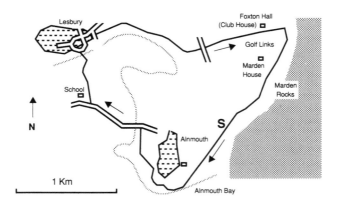

From the car park, next to the old lifeboat station, go right, towards the mouth of the
Aln. At first the way is along a dune track, but then bears left on to the beach and
follows the high tide mark. Bear right into the mouth of the estuary opposite a large
green mound across the river. Continue along the line of the building to the right of
the muddy estuary. Go through a children's playground into Garden Terrace and turn
left, briefly, then left again over a stile and along a path with a short wall on your left.
This will bring you to Duchesses Bridge: go up some steps, cross the road and turn
left over the footway. Stay on the right-hand side of the road as it bears right, and
where it bends left, short of a school, go through a wicket on the right. Cross the field
ahead close to the hedge on your right, leaving through another wicket. Continue with
the fence on your right for about 80 yards, past the end of some houses. There, bear
left to a road and turn right, along it, to go over a footbridge. On reaching Lesbury

68

turn right opposite the church, go along the main street and uphill to a road junction. Beyond this the road bears left. Here look for a footpath between two houses on the right. Turn on to it and go through a small gate into a field. Bear right, along the river, continuing alongside it across two fields. Turn left at stone telegraph poles and, keeping the line of poles slightly to your left, climb a short, steep hill to reach a road. Cross and go along a drive signposted 'Alnmouth Golf Club'. At the Golf Club, Foxton Hall, take the bramble-lined path to the left of the Members Car Park sign, which leads to the sea. Turn right on to the beach and follow the tideline, passing breakwaters, back to **Alnmouth** and the car park.

POINTS OF INTEREST:
Alnmouth – Once comparatively obscure, Alnmouth became famous because it stood at a strategic point between the dioceses of Hexham and Lindisfarne. St Cuthbert was probably there in 684 ad when he was elected Bishop of Hexham. The green hill seen across the Aln was almost certainly the site of a synod, described by Bede as 'Twyford' the place of two fords. It was once attached to the rest of the town, but in 1806 the river changed course and Alnmouth and the hill were parted.

REFRESHMENTS:
Available at Alnmouth and Lesbury.

Walk 32   **DODDINGTON MOOR**   4m (6.4km)

Maps: OS Sheets Landranger 75; Pathfinder NT 82/92 and NU 02/12.

A strenuous climb to start, but easy going for the most part.

Start: At 999325, on the left side of the Wooler – Berwick road just before the junction to Nesbitt.

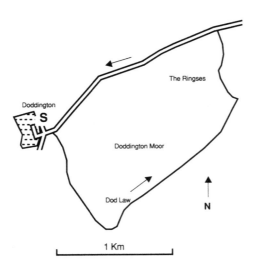

From the parking area, opposite a row of terraced cottages, go down the road towards Wooler for 100 yards, turn left by a well and go along a surfaced track signposted 'Wooler Golf Course'.

Cross a stile, signposted 'Dod Law' on the right in about 100 yards. Go up a grassy slope along the fence on your right for another 100 yards, then leave the fence and go half-left, up the hillside to a hawthorn hedge. Walk with the hedge on your right, going uphill to cross a stile. Go forward for 50 yards to reach the last thornbush. Turn left there, uphill, on a narrow path to pass just below a seat. Continue contouring below **Dod Law** to reach a cottage. Go right, around the cottage and outbuildings, and up a little walled field on the left. At the end of a wall, ignore the track and

70

continue along a narrow path which crosses another track to join a good path 100 yards further on. Continue along this path, going over a stile, and turn left at a cairn. Go downhill, following cairns, towards a small plantation. Go through two gates at the bottom of the slope and walk to the left corner of the plantation. Follow the wall on your right for $1/_4$ mile to reach a stile. Cross, turn left, along a mix of wall and fence on your left, and cross a field to reach a stile. Beyond, turn left along a track for $1/_2$ mile to a gate. Go through and turn right down a lane to the main road in **Doddington** where the walk began.

POINTS OF INTEREST:

Dod Law – There are lots of pre-historic remains around Dod Law, including at least five hillforts, hut circles and rock carvings. In 1984-85 Newcastle University excavated the outer rampart of the fort below which the route passes.

Doddington – Dodwell, the original Saxon settlement here grew up because there was a plentiful and reliable supply of springs. In the Lay Subsidy Rolls of 1296, Doddington, by then a sizeable Saxon village, was assessed for tax purposes at £65, a lot of money in those days. In 1538 the village equipped twelve men with horse and armour for the defence of the Border. In the early 18th century it had a weekly cattle mart, a quarry and several hand-loom weavers. Today it is just a cluster of cottages grouped around two large farms with a church. The Castle and Well are the only evidence of an important past.

Walk 33   **SWINHOPE VALLEY**   4m (6.4km)

Maps: OS Sheets Landranger 87; Pathfinder NY 84/94.

An exquisite little walk, especially lovely in early summer when the wild flowers are at their best or in the autumn when the hills are purple with heather.

Start: At 852478, Coalpits cottages, $^3/_4$ mile south of Sparty Lea.

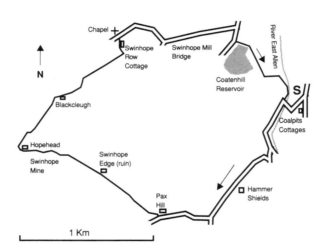

Go westwards from the road end, along the unclassified road to reach a footbridge and ford over the East Allen River. Cross and turn left along a road which runs beside the river for $^1/_3$ mile, then swings sharply upwards, passing Hammershields farm on the left, to join the Alston unclassified road at an old quarry. The road continues past Scotchmeadows Farm on the left and a minor crossroads at Guide Post Cottages, the last of which is now called Pax Hill. Just beyond Pax Hill go right, through a gate, and continue along a path diagonally across a field to a small gate in a facing wall. Go ahead, veering left, gradually, along a rather indistinct path to reach a stile over the next field wall. Continue in the same direction across the next field, and go through the remains of a gateway in a broken wall to reach Swinhope Edge, a ruinous farm.

There, an open gateway leads down to another gate. Go through, and cross a rough pasture to a gate at the bottom left of the field. Beyond is ruinous **Swinhope Mine**. At the east end of the mine cross a bridge, and at the end of a spoil heap go through a gate into rough wet pasture. Cross to Hope Head Farm. Go through the farm, using two gates, on to a rough surfaced track. Follow this north-eastwards for $^2/_3$ mile. Ignore the track which swings steeply to the left, and turn right at Blackcleugh farm buildings. In 40 yards the path crosses a burn by plank bridge and continues to Low Hayrake farm, going behind the buildings. Cross an access road and follow a fence to a stone stile at the edge of a plantation. Cross the stile and go through the plantation to reach Swinhope Shield Farm. Cross a stile into a field and, in 30 yards, turn left through a gate. Continue to Swinhope Row Cottage, join a minor road near a disused chapel and go right, along it. Cross Swinhope Mill bridge and turn right at a T-junction. After 100 yards cross a stone stile on the left near Coatenhill Reservoir. Follow a track, bearing right past the rear of a cottage, go through a gate and across the field in front of Coatenhill Farm to join the riverside path leading back to the ford and bridge near the start. Cross the bridge and go up the road to the start.

POINTS OF INTEREST:
Swinhope Mine – One of many small lead mines which were scattered over the area. It serves as a good landmark so if the path becomes indistinct there is no fear of losing the way.

Walk 34   **MONK WOOD**   4m (6.4km)

Maps: OS Sheets Landranger 87; Pathfinder NY 65/75.

A walk for late autumn when the leaves are turning and the views across the valley to the northwest are particularly good.

Start: At 793565, $\frac{1}{2}$ mile WSW of Keenley crossroads, towards Ninebanks, where the road bends south.

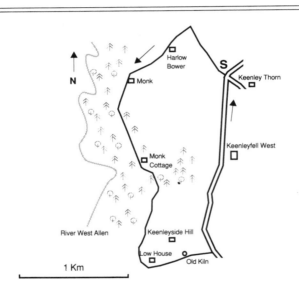

Go through a gate in the right-hand corner along the wall on the outside of the bend. Continue north-easterly along the edge of the field on your left and go through a gate into a quarried area, walking along a path that is boggy in places. Cross a wall stile into a lane and go left past Harlow Bower house. Where the lane ends go to the right of a shed and through a field gate set at an angle into a conifer plantation. Walk alongside a wall, and go through a wicket into a field. Continue, and cross the facing wall using a stile. Go half-right down the next field, following a line of electricity poles to a fence, which you cross by stile. Cross the farmyard to the right of **Monk Farm**, which is topped with a dovecote. Go alongside this building and past a tithe barn, continuing southwards along a clear track through Monk Wood. At Monk

Cottage, fork right, leaving the wood through a field gate, from where there is a good view of Blackett Bridge which crosses the West Allen on the right. Continue along a rather indistinct track, contouring a hill just below a wall and curving up to the left to pass through a gate below Low House. Do not take the left turn beyond it, which leads only to Keenleyside Farm: instead, bear left along an uphill route past a lime kiln and then go along an enclosed track to reach a road through a field gate. Turn left, to reach the starting place.

POINTS OF INTEREST:

Monk Farm – The Monk buildings were originally a 16th century fortified farmhouse. The wall on which the dovecote sits is $4^1/_2$ feet thick, and was probably once a chimney stack. The farm is traditionally connected with the monks of Hexham Priory.

Walk 35   **BROCOLITIA AND UPPERTOWN**   4m (6.4km)

Maps: OS Sheets Landranger 87; Pathfinder NY 86/96.

Easy going over fields, through woods and along a drove road.

Start: At 861714, Brocolitia car park.

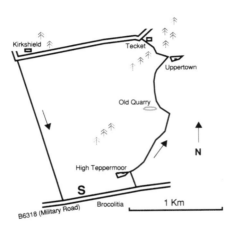

From the car park, turn right and go for 400 yards along the **Military Road**. Turn left, as directed by a 'To Uppertown', sign to reach High Teppermoor Farm. Cross the stile where the track ends. Turn right at the end of some buildings, aiming for the nearer of two gates, which is waymarked. Follow a track diagonally across the field ahead to reach another gate. Stay on the track, going along the left side of a wood to the far end of the field. Turn left, alongside a wall, to reach a ladder stile. Go down a steep path to a stile at the bottom, climb over it and follow a track close to a field boundary on the right, going through two gates. At the second gate turn right to Uppertown and, just before the buildings, turn left at a ruin and continue along a cart track. Go through a gate, over a farm track and enter a wood via a wicket. Take the track to a footbridge over Crook Burn. Cross the bridge and climb the bank opposite. On reaching a surfaced road turn left and continue to Kirkshield. Turn left at the end of the road, along a track leading south to the Military Road. Turn left back to the car park.

POINTS OF INTEREST:

Military Road – General Wade's Road at Brocolitia, as on many lengths of the Wall, is built right on top of it. It was here, during the 1745 rebellion that when Bonnie Prince Charlie's forces came to Carlisle on their journey south they escaped the English forces of the King, stationed at Newcastle under the command of Wade, because no road between Newcastle and Carlisle was in good enough shape to carry his artillery. He had to wait and go south to intercept the invaders. Consequently, Wade directed that a good road be built across this narrowest section of the country to create a fast route between the east and west coasts. It has always been called Wade's Road or the Military Road. Miles and miles of Hadrian's Wall were demolished to form its base because it had to be strong enough to carry military traffic. The road building began in 1751, despite some opposition, and travellers using it since its completion have thanked Wade for providing such an excellent route. The General died before it was started.

Walk 36　　**STEEL RIGG AND HOTBANK**　　4m (6.4km)

Maps: OS Sheets Landranger 87; Pathfinder NY 66/76.

A walk that goes north of the Wall, and then along it, offering the views the 'barbarians' had of it and the Romans had from it.

Start: At 751677, Steel Rigg car park.

From the main entrance of the car park turn right along the road for 200 yards to reach a finger post signed 'Hotbank $1\frac{1}{2}$m' on the right. Cross a stile and go along a farm track, passing Peatrigg barn to reach Long Side barn. Continue to a waymarked wall. Cross the stile with a sheepfold on the left, then go ahead to reach a ditch. Bear right at a sike and turn left over it at a waymarker. Aim for the left-hand edge of Hotbank Crags and, after the second stile, go through a gate and along a track to Hotbank Farm. Cross the farmyard and go over a stile beside a gate. Turn right and follow the line of the Wall, heading west. Go on to a farm track, then go right over a stile alongside a cattle grid to the north side of the Wall. Cross a ladder stile into a wood and go to the top of the crags above **Crag Lough**.

　　The way ahead is now well-defined, going alongside the Wall. Descend the steep west end of Peel Crags using steps, and from the bottom follow the path back to the car park.

POINTS OF INTEREST:

Crag Lough – It was near here that a most extraordinary man, writing in 1801, noted that a stretch of wall, 8ft high was still standing. The man was William Hutton and in 1801, aged 78, he walked the full length of the Wall having first walked from Birmingham to the Lake District. He walked the Wall in both directions, then walked all the way back to Birmingham, a distance of 600 miles. Throughout he wore a black suit, carried a bag, an umbrella and an inkhorn. One pair of shoes lasted him the whole journey and his socks were scarcely holed. His daughter, Catherine, accompanied him throughout. Each morning he rose at four and walked to the next stage. Catherine rose at seven, and, following by horse, joined him for breakfast. He then rested for two hours before setting off again while she rode ahead seeking dinner and lodgings for the night. At times the weather was so hot he had to undo the buttons on his waistcoat.

Scots Pine and Sycamore predominate in Crag Lough Wood, with Rowan and Hazel finding a precarious anchorage on the crags themselves.

REFRESHMENTS:

The Twice Brewed Inn (tel no: 0434 344534) about $^1/_2$ mile south from the car park at the start, on the Military Road.

Walk 37   **OLD BEWICK AND BLAWEARIE**   4m (6.4km)
Maps: OS Sheets Landranger 75; Pathfinder NU 02/12.
A superb walk to remote and eerily ruinous Blawearie.
Start: At 066215, Old Bewick.

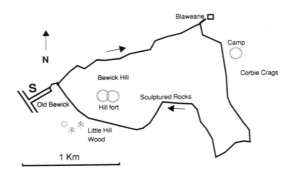

From Old Bewick go north-east along a stony side-road, past terraced houses on the left. The road leads through a gate on to a moor. Go along a track, with Bewick Hill on the right, and through two gates. The enclosed land ends at a wicket beside a replaced gateway: go through it and follow the track ahead across moorland to Blawearie. From the ruin, retrace your steps for 50 yards and turn left, over a burn. Bear left round the lower slope of a small hill, aiming for a cairn on the hill close to the remains of a Romano-British camp. Continue along a grassy path towards a radio mast on the skyline ahead. Bear right, on to the ridge between Harehope Burn and Stock Brook and soon descend to an alder grove on the banks of Harehope. Keep to the right of the burn, making for a gate in the fence. Tun right just before the gate and walk uphill, between Tick Law and Harehope Hill. The faint track goes between two old hawthorns visible on the skyline. Where a fence cuts the line of the track, turn right before the gate in it and walk alongside the fence to the next gate. Here turn right along a rutted bridleway which bears to the left and climbs to Tick Law. Stay on the bridleway, with the fence visible to the left, to a point where the fence bears left. At that point the fence line is followed to a wicket in a stone wall. Go through and bear half-left. Descend a hillside and bear right along its lower slope, following a path to the right of a small plantation. Stay on the same contour: do not go along the line of the fence, but stay about halfway up the slope. Go to the lower edge of the pines beneath Hanging Crag and continue to a fence. Cross a stile in it and turn left back to **Old Bewick**.

POINTS OF INTEREST:

Old Bewick – The name Bewick probably derived from the Old English Bes-wic, meaning bee-farm. The first Lord of Bewick was called Arkle Moreal. He was granted the Lordship in 1093 after slaying Malcolm, King of Scotland. His gratitude to the king was short lived, in 1095 he took part in an insurrection and his lands were confiscated.

Walk 38 PARK BURNFOOT AND BELLISTER CASTLE 4m (6.4km)

Maps: OS Sheets Landranger 87; Pathfinder NY 66/76.

A fine walk that begins and ends in woodland.

Start: At 684620, a pull-in just before Park Burnfoot Farm.

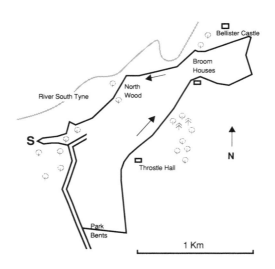

From the pull-in on the south of the road go uphill for 50 yards and then enter a wood over a stile. Turn right along a waymarked path and follow it to a road. Turn left. Go right at a junction and continue into **Park** village. Leave the village over the bridge across the railway track, returning to the main road at a junction. Turn right for 200 yards, and then turn left through a gate at Park Bents. Follow a farm road towards Linn Shield. Cross a cattle grid and, just before the next gate, turn left along a track, going alongside the wall on the right. Go through a gate and take a track that goes gently uphill and bears slightly left. Go through a gate and continue along a field track. Go through another gate and approach Throstle Hall, on the right. Walk to the left of the Hall, then go downhill and across a field bottom, with a railway cutting on the left. Go towards a gate at the far end of the field. Go through and take a path over a railway bridge. Turn right to Broom Houses, leaving them through the middle, waymarked, gate. Take the path over the railway and go through two metal gates. Turn left through the next gate in the wall. Turn right and walk for 200 yards along a field top. Turn left towards stiles on each side of the railway track. Beyond the track go straight ahead to reach a hilltop stile. Cross and go diagonally right to the eastern end of the wood ahead. Follow waymarkers through the wood, leaving it through a gate. Cross a road and enter a wooded riverbank. Follow a waymarked path through the wood and a National Trust camp site to reach the start.

POINTS OF INTEREST:

Park – Many of the houses in the village are owned by the Bellister Estate: the oldest is dated 1711. Most of the building stone was brought from the quarry just south of the village, which explains the uniformity. The quarry was an Awarded Quarry, ie. stone was given to the villagers for their use, so it was readily available. During the last century crofting was the local way of life, and the houses were built to accommodate the beasts below stairs, with the people living above. The heat from the cattle warmed the upper rooms: if you wanted to turn the heating down you let the cattle out to pasture.

REFRESHMENTS:

None en route, but there are hotels, pubs and cafés in nearby Haltwhistle.

Walk 39   **HOUSESTEADS, KING'S WICKET AND HOTBANK**   4m (6.4km)

Maps: OS Sheets Landranger 87; Pathfinder NY 66/76.

Four Northumbrian loughs can be seen from this walk along Hadrian's Wall.

Start: At 795684, Housesteads car park on the B6318.

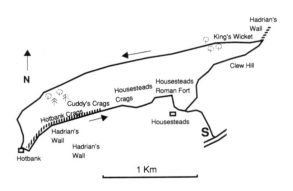

From the car park go northwards, past an Information Barn, and follow a track to Housesteads Fort. If you wish to look around the fort and the museum, an admission charge is payable. Our walk skirts the south side of the fort and continues along the Wall to Knag Burn. Cross the burn on a stone bridge. Go uphill, with the Wall on your left, to cross a stile, at the north-east corner of a field, into Housesteads Plantation. Leave over a stile at the eastern end and follow a track eastwards over Clew Hill and King's Hill. Beyond King's Hill descend to reach a stile. Cross and follow the path which now heads westwards, crossing a hollow towards a new plantation. Continue along the ridge, following waymarkers. Enter the plantation over a stile and exit over another. Continue due west, passing a sheep fold, to reach a gate and stile in a field

84

wall. Cross the Pennine Way stile and continue along a clear track to a limekiln. Continue westwards to Hotbank. Cross the farmyard and leave over a stile, rejoining the line of the Wall. Turn left and go east, with the Wall on your left, back to the edge of Housesteads Fort. Go between the fort and the museum to reach the track that passes **Housesteads** on its way back to the car park.

POINTS OF INTEREST:

Housesteads – For many years Housesteads was the seat of the Armstrongs, as bloodthirsty a bunch of villains as were to be found in the Borders They sold Housesteads in the 17th century for about £50 and emigrated to America. John Clayton of Chesters bought it in the 19th century and his family conveyed it to the National Trust in 1974. The fort itself is in the guardianship of the English Heritage.

Walk 40   **KIRKNEWTON AND COLLEGE BURN**   4m (6.4km)

Maps: OS Sheets Landranger 75; Pathfinder NU 02/12.

A short scramble down a grassy bank, some burnside walking and no steep hills.

Start: At 914303, beside the B6351, just to the east of Kirknewton church.

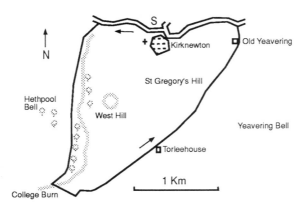

From the grass verge parking area go westwards, along the road as far as a railway house on the right. Pass this, go over a road bridge and cross the stone stile on the left at its end. Walk along the bank of **College Burn**. Cross a stile over an electrified fence, walk below a low cliff and across a wide, grassy flat area to reach a gate. Go through the gate and up a slope. Go through another gate and over a ladder stile. Walk along a path above the trees. The path contours round the hillside, passing below rocky screes on the right, to reach a gate in a wall.

    The trees on Hethpool Bell, to the right, are oaks planted by Admiral Collingwood who inherited the estate through his wife. He was raised to the peerage for his services at the Battle of Trafalgar in 1805. He took the title Baron Collingwood of Hethpool and Coldburn. Although Hethpool was not his main residence, he took a great interest in it and hoped that the oaks he grew there would eventually provide timber for his ships.

Turn left, down a grassy bank to cross the bridge on the left. Cheviot wild goats roam the hills across the burn. These goats, which cannot be approached closely, are thought to be the descendants of animals brought to the hillsides by shepherds centuries ago. The true wild goat has never been an indigenous British mammal.

Once over the bridge turn left, cross a stile and go uphill. Continue ahead for 250 yards to join a path which leads down to an easy crossing of the gully on the left. Go out of the gully, turn half right and cross a stile. Go uphill to join a farm track just before a sheepfold. Turn left along the track to Torlee House. Pass in front of the house, and continue through several gates. Yeavering Bell, on the right, has, on its summit, the remains of the largest hill fort in Northumberland. Continue along the track, passing in front of the cottages of Old Yeavering, to reach the main road. Turn left to return to **Kirknewton**.

POINTS OF INTEREST:

College Burn – In 1556 this burn was called 'Colleche', a name derived from the Anglo-Saxon 'col' and 'leche', meaning a stream flowing through boggy land.
Kirknewton – In 1336 Kirknewton was called New Town. It suffered repeatedly from depredations by the Scots during the years of the Border Raids. A refuge tower had been built by 1415 and was still standing in 1554.

Walk 41 THE HARTHOPE VALLEY AND NORTH MIDDLETON

4m (6.4km)

Maps: OS Sheets Landranger 75; Pathfinder NT 82/92.

A fine walk with a return through pretty Happy Valley.

Start: At 976250, the grassy space on the right, just before the first bridge in Harthope valley.

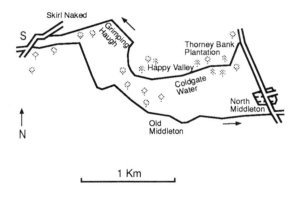

From the car park cross the first bridge in the valley and go along the road, briefly, to reach a signposted stile on the left. Go over and follow the fence on your right to Harthope Burn. Dippers are frequently seen along the Burn: they are easily identified by their white breasts, their nervous bobbing and their 'zit, zit, zit' call notes. They feed on aquatic insects, walking under water with their wings partly open, and are very territorial. Cross the burn, climb the slope ahead and, still with the fence on your right, continue around the hillside to cross a stile beside a wicket. Beyond a gap in a wall turn right. The shepherds cottage, seen above the trees on the left is called Skirl Naked. Locals call it 'Skirlie'. At the turn of the century there was talk of changing the name to Shining Pool, but nothing came of it and the original name remains.

Walk up the slope on a clear path, go through a gate and continue along a green track to reach an old wall and a fence. Turn left, downhill, to reach a fence corner with two gates. The burn below is Coldgate Water which began as Harthope Burn. A bit lower downstream, just past Coldgate Ford, it becomes Wooler Water and flows past Wooler to join the River Till. Hereabouts burns frequently change their names en route to a larger river. Go through the right-hand gate and continue along the path above the valley. Stay close to the fence on the left to reach a stile and a bridge. The bridge was built in 1979 by the National Park Area Warden assisted by Voluntary Wardens, about 200 of whom patrol 'honey pot' localities during the holiday season.

Cross the bridge and go up the slope. Turn left and follow a track down to a road. Turn left, go through **North Middleton** hamlet and on to reach a ford. Cross the bridge, turn left and enter Happy Valley, following a path which crosses fields along the valley bottom. After $1/_2$ mile the path climbs a gentle slope and continues through gorse bushes close to a burn on the left. Continue along the flat land back to the parking area.

POINTS OF INTEREST:

North Middleton – Middleton is a very common Old English place name and means 'middle village' or 'homestead'. There are several examples of it in Northumberland.

Walk 42   **THE DUCHESS TRAIL** $4^1/_4$m (6.8km)

Maps: OS Sheets Landranger 80; Pathfinder NY 69/79.

A walk entirely in Kielder Forest, one of the largest man-made forests in Europe.

Start: At 631934, Kielder Castle car park.

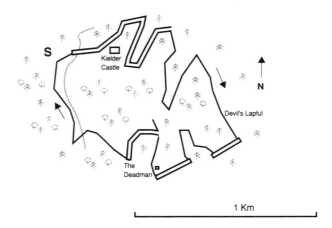

1 Km

From the car park turn right, down the hill, and at the bottom turn left along a path leading to **Kielder Castle**. Go right in front of the castle to reach a notice, signed for the **Duchess Trail**. From there go left to the riverbank and continue along it to a bridge. Cross and follow yellow arrows along a path to the right. On reaching a broken wall, go through a gap in it and uphill along a higher path that curves left and contours the hillside. When a wall is reached go along its right side. When it ends continue for a few yards, and then turn right, uphill, on a narrow path to reach a higher forest road. Turn right. After $^1/_2$ mile turn half-left at a T-junction, then half-right at the first forest road on that side. At the hilltop, cross a firebreak and continue along a level section of road. The cairn on the right in a small clearing is the Devil's Lapful. Continue along the forest road for 300 yards past the Devil's Lapful and then turn right, down a

90

firebreak. Should you miss this turning the forest road you are on bends left soon afterwards. Descend to a forest road and turn right.

At a T-junction turn left for 200 yards, then go right, along a second firebreak. Descend into a small valley and climb the far side of it to reach a forest road, passing, on the right, another cairn, the Deadman. Turn right and after about $\frac{1}{4}$ mile, where the forest road bends left, leave it, also going left, on to a firebreak, following yellow and orange arrows. Continue along a lovely path, following the arrows, to reach a small gate. Go through it and half-left, down a field to reach a gate leading to a road. Go right to a T-junction. Go left over a bridge, and immediately turn right along the left bank of the river. Soon a road is reached: go half-left to reach a minor road which leads back to the car park.

POINTS OF INTEREST:

Kielder Castle – Built as a hunting Lodge for Earl Percy the Duke of Northumberland, between 1772 and 1775.

Duchess Trail – The trail is based on a drive that a Duchess of Northumberland had constructed so that she could while away the time while her husband was out hunting.

Walk 43   **HOLY ISLAND** $4^1/_2$m (7.2km)

Maps: OS Sheets Landranger 75; Pathfinder NU 04/14.

*A walk at its best in winter, when most of the visitors have left
and the over-wintering waders and wildfowl have arrived.*

Start: At 128421, the main village car park.

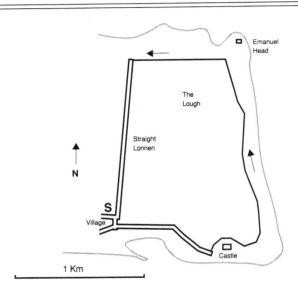

Go on to the road and turn left into Sandham Lane. Turn right and continue to a T-
junction. Turn left and go directly towards Lindisfarne Castle, moving parallel to the
shoreline. Just before the castle go through a small gate. The castle entrance is up a
cobbled path to the right but our walk forks left, past the castle, to reach the sea wall
over a bridge. Continue along the shoreline, curving left to reach another small gate.
Follow the clear path which runs to the right of a fence for $^3/_4$ mile to reach a stile near
a small lake, the Lough. Cross and walk to a wall. Cross this and turn left along a path
which runs beside the wall at first, and then beside a fence. After nearly $^1/_2$ mile a lane,
Straight Lonnen, is reached. Turn left along it to go back to **Lindisfarne** village and
the car park.

POINTS OF INTEREST:

Lindisfarne – Can only be reached by vehicle by crossing the Causeway from the mainland. This causeway is covered at high tide and it is dangerous to attempt to cross around these times. As a general rule, the causeway is not fordable for a period from approximately 2 hours before to $3\frac{1}{2}$ hours after each high tide. Information about this can be obtained from local Information Centres and from notices at each end of the Causeway.

REFRESHMENTS:

There are cafés and pubs in the village.

Walk 44   **CRASTER AND HOWICK** $4^1/_2$m (7.2km)
Maps: OS Sheets Landranger 81; Pathfinder NU 21/22.
*A nice walk, with pasture, the richly wooded Howick Hall estate
and a fine, rocky shore.*
Start: At 256197, Craster car park, within the shell of the Old
Craster Quarry.

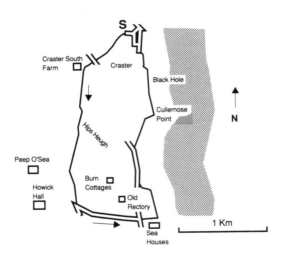

Take the path, right, from behind the displays at the car park, and go through an area
of scrub and thorny woodland with the now-wooded quarry face on your left. Bear
left along the bottom track at the first junction, bear right at the second junction, to
reach a field. Cross this with Craster South Farm ahead. Go through a gate, cross the
road and go along a side road to Craster South Farm. Continue to the right of a terrace
of cottages, beyond which the path leads half-left through a gate into a field corner.
Continue along the edge of the field, exiting through a gate and follow a climbing
path to Hips Heugh, a craggy hilltop. The path bears left as the field narrows and a
wall replaces a hawthorn hedge. Cross a stile at the end of the field and bear right

below the face of Hips Heugh. The path goes along the wall on the right to reach a stile beside a gate. Cross and traverse the field ahead, bearing slightly left, to reach a gate near some elms. Go through and walk along the right side of the field ahead, with Peep O'Sea Farm seen ahead. Go through a gate, then turn sharp right into the field corner. In a dip of the land a track cuts through a belt of trees and leads to a gate. Go through this gate and continue up the track. Go over the brow of a hill and through another gate on to a surfaced track. The track follows a wall to a road. Turn left past the turning to Howick village, and continue over the brow of a hill. When the road turns sharp left, go straight ahead towards the sea, following a signpost 'Coastal Path, Craster 2'. At the end of the track turn left along the coastal footpath going above a cliff to meet the Craster Road. Go parallel to the road for a while, cutting through scrub where it bears right towards Cullernose Point. Continue along a gravelled path that descends towards Cullernose. Continue northwards along the path, soon turning abruptly left and then bearing right to regain the coastline. Cross a stile and continue to a football field. Go left to a road, at the far end of which turn right, then left into Craster. Take the road inland, going left around the Inshore Lifeboat Station. After 200 yards the car park is reached on the left.

Walk 45   THE HARTHOPE VALLEY AND OLD MIDDLETON

4$^{1}/_{2}$m (7.2km)

Maps: OS Sheets Landranger 75; Pathfinder NU 02/12.

Easy walking with good views of the Harthope Valley.

Start: At 976250, a parking space on the right of the first bridge in Harthope Valley.

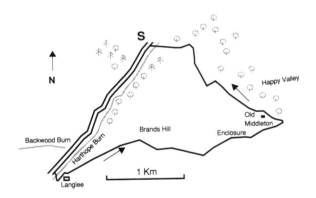

From the grassy car parking area cross the bridge over Carey Burn. The bridge was built in 1956 to replace a large wooden one and a small stone footbridge, both of which had been washed away in the floods of 1948. Go along the road for about a mile to reach a cottage. Cross Harthope Burn on a bridge, go in front of the cottage garden and along the uphill path. Near the top, cross a track and walk to the gate on the skyline. Go through and along a grassy path towards a ruinous walled enclosure on the right. When the path bifurcates about 100 yards short of the enclosure, take the left fork. Walk downhill, cross a track and continue to reach a fence near some sheep pens on the right. Cross a ladder stile and go over the field ahead staying close to the fence on the right. Cross the next two stiles and go in front of a **cottage**. Continue along a track, going over a burn and, short of a facing wall, turn left and cross a footbridge and a stile. Cross the field ahead near the fence on your right. Go over a stile and walk beside the plantation on your right. Follow the line of an old hedge on your left, keeping well above Happy Valley. Turn left, uphill, at a gate and go along a clear grassy track staying close to the hedge on your left. As the track levels, turn right along an indistinct grassy track. After 300 yards the track bears right, downhill, and reaches a gate. Go through this gate, turn half left, cross a sike and descend to a fence corner. Turn left to cross a stile next to a wicket. Continue around the hillside, keeping the fence on your left. At a point above a meeting of the Carey and Harthope Burns cross a footbridge and continue to the valley road. Turn right to return to the start.

POINTS OF INTEREST:

Cottage – The shepherd's cottage is all that remains of Old Middleton. In medieval times it was a village consisting of the Lord of the Manor, two or three free tenants, a few dozen villein farmers and about half a dozen cottagers. Most of the population lived on isolated farms or in a township. The suffix 'tun' is Old English for a homestead. The townships were divided into farms of 30 or 50 acres. They were self-sufficient, having their own bakery and tannery, and the use of the lord's mill. Turbary rights enabled them to cut turf for roofing. Spinning and weaving were home industries.

Walk 46   SPARTY LEA AND SWINHOPE   4¹/₂m (7.2km)
Maps: OS Sheets Landranger 87; Pathfinder NY 84/94.
*A pleasant walk by riverside, along quiet roads and over fields,
through a former lead mining area.*
Start: At 850490, opposite Sparty Lea Methodist Church on the
B6295.

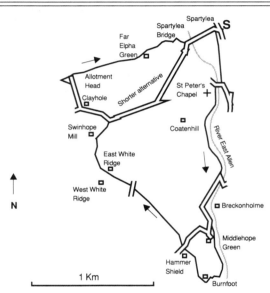

From the signpost, 'To the Cornmill', descend the steps and continue south, crossing
two fields. Go over a stile on to a road. Cross a bridge and go towards a wicket beside
the disused **Chapelry of St Peter's**. Follow a sign, going through a gate and keeping
the river on your left. Where the track fades, cross a stone stile into a field. Bear left
through a gate and go over a stile. Continue along the line of the river to reach a gate
with a stile beside it, with the drive to Coatenmill, behind you. Go along the tarmac
road, upstream, passing, on the far bank, the lead mining remains of Breckonholme.
Continue past a ford and a footbridge and watch for the sign 'Pease Meadows'. Follow
the riverside path. Pass a water pipe bridge and, after 200 yards, a bridge to Pease
Meadows. Do not cross the river: instead, turn right, over a stile, away from the river,

aiming for the outbuildings at the extreme left of Burnfoot Farm. Cross a stile near a barn wall and take the path uphill, going north-west towards a gate. Go through and continue uphill to the right of Hammershields Farm. Cross a stile on to a road, and cross another stile opposite signposted for 'White Ridge', about $\frac{1}{2}$ mile distant.

Go diagonally across fields on a clear path, leaving through a gate on to a minor road. Turn right to reach a gate on the left for White Ridge. Go to the left of East White Ridge, using stiles and a footbridge to reach Swinhope Mill. Go in front of the farm, with the buildings on your left and the burn on your right, to reach Swinhope road. From here either turn right, soon crossing an iron bridge, and then turn left at a T-junction to return to the start; or, turn left along the road to Clayhole Farm, turning right there and going over fields via Far Elpha Green, crossing Swinhope Beck and turning left over Sparty Lea Bridge to reach the start.

POINTS OF INTEREST:

Chapelry of St Peter's – The now disused chapel was built before 1124, rebuilt in 1825 and repaired in 1899.

Walk 47   **HAPPY VALLEY**   4¹/₂m (7.2km)

Maps: OS Sheets Landranger 75; Pathfinder NT 82/92.

This lovely walk follows grassy paths above Coldgate Water to North Middleton.

Start: At 977250, on the wide grass verge on the Wooler side of the bridge near Skirl Naked.

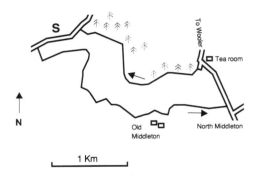

Cross the nearby bridge and, where the fence ends on the left, go left over a stile signposted 'Middleton Old Town – North and South Middleton'. Cross a footbridge, climb some steps and follow a clear path across the hillside overlooking the river and the parking area.

Go through a small gate in a fence and, in a few yards, go right, up the hillside to a gate. Keep climbing until the path curves left to contour the hillside. On reaching a broken wall with yellow arrows turn left, downhill, to reach a fence. Turn right, along a path to a stile at the corner of a wood and go alongside it to a further stile at its far end, on the left. Go around the edge of the field to a third stile. Cross and descend, half-left, to a footbridge. Go over and follow a farm road. Turn left, through a gate and go down the farm road to reach the road at North Middleton. Turn left back to the car park.

POINTS OF INTEREST:

Old Middleton – a ruinous small cottage, stands on the site of Old Middleton or Middleton Old Town, a deserted village. Thousands of villages and hamlets like Old Middleton have vanished down the ages.

REFRESHMENTS:

The Happy Valley Tea Rooms, near the ford and footbridge to the north of North Middleton.

Walk 48   **THE HOPE AND COSE HOLE**   4¹/₂m (7.2km)
Maps: OS Sheets Landranger 87; Pathfinder NY 85/95.
A pleasant walk which touches the Allendale end of the Blackett Level.
Start: At 839559, Allendale Town Post Office.

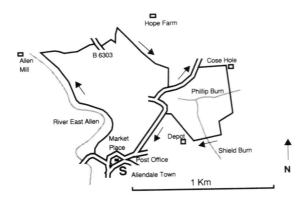

From the Post Office descend Peth Bank and turn right at a footpath sign. Follow the footpath along the east bank of the River East Allen, passing, in about 300 yards, a ruinous building that marks the Allendale end of the **Blackett Level**. Cross a footbridge beyond it and continue along the riverbank for a further ¹/₂ mile. On approaching the main road, fork right, through a wicket and continue eastwards through fields to reach stone steps leading to the B6303, the Allendale – Hexham road. Turn right along it, briefly, then go left, along a rough track between houses. The track climbs steeply and bears right, then goes sharp left. In less than ¹/₂ mile turn right, through a gate and go south-eastwards across fields. The route descends, going through trees and between a red brick house and a bungalow at a minor road. Turn left along this road, past some houses on the right, for 300 yards to reach a gate on your right at a signpost. Go through and cross a field to disused Cose Hole farmhouse. Turn sharp right and descend, due south, to a stream which is crossed on a stone bridge. Climb the hillside to a stile, go over, and continue climbing (it is steeper now) until you can see Portgate Farm above and to your left. Do not go to the farm: instead, go downhill, westwards, staying parallel to a fence, to reach some steps which lead downhill to another bridge over a stream. Climb more steps and, just before reaching the road at the end of the footpath, turn sharp right, alongside the boundary wall of the Council Depot, to reach the main Allendale road at The Dene. Turn left back into Allendale Town.

POINTS OF INTEREST:

Blackett Level – Planned by Sopwith, the mining engineer to Blackett-Beaumont, who owned the lead mines. It was intended to run for 7 miles from Allendale to Allenheads and work on it began on 4th October 1855. In 1896 and with only $4^1/_2$ miles of the projected tunnel completed, work on it was abandoned. The object of the exercise was to find new veins of lead in the valley and draw off the water from the mines at Allenheads. The project was only partly successful and cost the, then enormous sum of £120,000.

REFRESHMENTS:

There are several possibilities in Allendale.

Walk 49   **DUNSTAN STEADS AND CRASTER** $4^1/_2$m (7.2km)
Maps: OS Sheets Landranger 75; Pathfinder NU 21/22.
An easy, grassland walk dominated by the sea and the remains
of Dunstanburgh castle.
Start: At 243223, on the verge just down the road from Dunstan
Steads Farm.

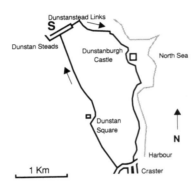

Go to the road end and through a gate leading to the dunes. Continue straight across
the golf course towards a gap in the dune ridge. Walk long the high tide mark until
sand gives way to boulders, at which point climb the dune ridge and continue along a
path to a wicket. Beyond, the path approaches the cliffs and **Dunstanburgh Castle**.
Follow the path as far as the keep of the castle and continue south down a grassy
hillside. Go alongside a sandy bay called Nova Scotia, beyond which keep going
south into Craster village where the path ends at a gate. Follow the road beyond,
which passes the harbour.

Take the main road, right, out of the village and opposite the car park take the
footpath on the right, signed 'Dunstan Square 1m'. After a wicket continue along this

path with the ridge to your right and a hedge to the left. At the end of the hedge go through a wicket and turn left. After another gate continue to Dunstan Square. Turn right at the farm, along a bridleway signed 'Dunstan Steads'. Go through a gate and along a concrete trackway. At a cattle grid the wall changes from the right side of the path to the left: continue north, past a small plantation. Cross a cattle grid to reach Dunstan Steads. Go through the farm and turn right at the road to return to the start.

POINTS OF INTEREST:

Dunstanburgh Castle – Started in 1313 by Thomas, second Earl of Lancaster, and completed around 1316. Thomas was executed by Edward II only 6 years later, following the Battle of Boroughbridge, and John of Gaunt brought the castle up to fighting trim for the Border Wars of the 1380's. It later became an important Lancastrian stronghold during the Wars of the Roses, but fell into decay after 1470.

REFRESHMENTS:

The Jolly Fisherman, Craster (tel no: 066576 218).
The Blue Bell Inn, Embleton (tel no: 066576 6398).
The Grey Inn, Embleton (tel no: 066576 237).
The Dunstanburgh Castle Hotel, Embleton (tel no: 066576 203).

Walk 50   **HARTSIDE AND COBDEN** $4^1/_2$m (7.2km)
Maps: OS Sheets Landranger 81; Pathfinder NT 81/91.
A short, uphill stretch followed by the crossing of a level grassy
area with good views.
Start: At 977162, on the roadside near Hartside Farm close to a
sign to Alnhammoor.

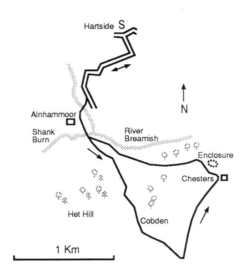

From Hartside Farm, and the left turn to Alnhammoor, go along the Alnhammoor
road to a bridge over the River Breamish. Cross the bridge and continue along the
road for 100 yards to reach a left turn. Cross a grassy slope in front of a cottage to
reach a gate in a wall. Go through and turn left, along a track. Go through a gate and
turn right by a bridge over Shank Burn. This quiet tree-lined stretch of water, where
Shank Burn and the River Breamish meet, is favoured by goosanders which nest in
holes in the trees or in the riverbank. Their bills are finely serrated which enables
them to hold slippery fish.

     Continue to a stile at a gate and bear right, across a field to reach a gate on a
slope near some trees. Continue up the hillside on a clear track, passing a sheepfold

on the left. Near the top of the slope an old mountain ash is passed on the right: prevailing winds have given it a slant. The mountain ash, which has no relationship to the ash proper, is also called the rowan, a name derived from the Norse 'runa', a charm. It has long been associated with witchcraft. Follow the clear track to the right corner of a plantation, cross a stile near a gate and continue along a sunken track. This climbs at first, then levels out to reach a ford. Walk in the same direction, on slightly rising ground, for 130 yards, to reach a farm road. Turn left along it to reach a gate. Continue towards a cottage, and when about 40 yards short of it, turn left along an indistinct path that climbs over a ridge to reach a wicket. Go through and walk left to another wicket. Beyond this follow the path through a plantation to reach a field, and cross it to the fence on the right. Follow the fence to the confluence of Shank Burn and the River Breamish. From there retrace your steps to the start near Hartside.

POINTS OF INTEREST:

The ancient enclosure passed soon after leaving the cottage of Chesters, now used by Scouts, contained a number of huts built during the Roman occupation of Britain. The huts were built of stone with conical roofs thatched with turf or heather. Wattle screens divided the interiors into small rooms.

Walk 51   ONCE BREWED AND WINSHIELD'S CRAGS $4^1/_2$m (7.2km)

Maps: OS Sheets Landranger 86; Pathfinder NY 66/76.

Roman Wall Country at its very best.

Start: At 753675, the Once Brewed Information Centre car park.

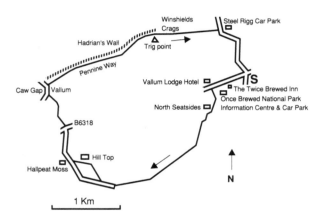

From the car park go back to the B6318 and go left, along it, for $^1/_4$ mile. Almost opposite Vallum Lodge Hotel, turn left beside a shed and cross a waymarked stile in a fence. Continue along the edge of the field ahead and cross a stile at its bottom. Go over Blackies Burn on a plank bridge and bear right, aiming for North Seatsides, a roofless ruin. Pass to the left of it. Continue south-westerly, half right, across the field ahead on rising ground, aiming for two stiles in the wire fences on your right. Cross both, and go up the next field, following yellow arrows and aiming for a barn at its far end. Cross a nearby stile and follow a waymarked post, half right, across a rough pasture to reach a ruinous wall. Keep in the same direction to the far corner of the field and cross a stile signposted 'Once Brewed'. Turn right along a farm road, and at the end of it cross a stile left of a gate on to the Melkridge road. Turn right to reach the B6318. Cross to a stile signposted 'Shield On the Wall'. Cross and follow a farm track. Where the wall ends, turn left briefly, and bear right as directed by a yellow arrow into the Wall's vallum. Climb out of it and go left along a waymarked path. Go round the foot of a ridge and over a ladder stile on to a road at Caw Gap. Go right, along the road, briefly, and through a kissing gate on your right, signposted 'Steel Rigg 2 miles'. You are now on the Pennine Way which hereabouts follows the line of Hadrian's Wall. Continue eastwards along it, ascending and descending at first before levelling out at the summit of **Winshield's Crags**. From the trig point continue eastwards along the Wall to reach a minor road near Steel Rigg car park. Turn right for $\frac{1}{2}$ mile, to cross the **B6318** and return to Once Brewed car park.

POINTS OF INTEREST:
Winshield's Crags – At 1,260ft above sea level the trig point on Winshield's Crags is the highest point along Hadrian's Wall. From it extensive views embrace Cross Fell, the Cheviots, the Tyne Valley, the Solway and a little bit of Scotland.
B6318 – The B6318 is the Roman Military road that served the Wall.

REFRESHMENTS:
The Twice Brewed Inn (tel no: 0434 344534) on the B6318.

Walk 52   **LOW PRUDHOE AND HORSLEY**   5m (8km)

Maps: OS Sheets Landranger 88; Pathfinder NZ 06/16.

A pleasant exploration of the Tyne Valley.

Start: At 087635, Low Prudhoe car park.

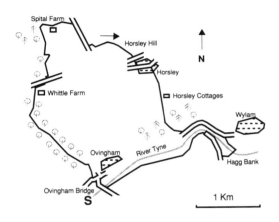

From the car park go left, crossing the Tyne over Ovingham Bridge, and turn left along a lane behind **Ovingham Church**. Cross a stile signposted 'Whittle Dene' and continue across a paddock. Cross a stile, and where the path bifurcates, go left alongside Whittle Burn into Whittle Dene. Continue upstream, along a clear path, going through a clearing, between holiday chalets, and past the ruinous Whittle Mill. The path climbs gradually through the wood – it can be muddy here – close to Whittle Burn. On reaching a footbridge do not cross it: instead, climb steeply to the eastern edge of the wood and turn left along the wood's edge, going below a sandstone outcrop and making a slippery 10 foot descent at a landslip. Walk to a concrete farm road and follow it as it turns right, parallel to the A69, then goes left to bridge it. Cross a stile at the second gate, and follow a farm track across two fields. At the top of the second, turn right along a fenced scarp overlooking Whittle Burn. Cross the stile ahead and cross Whittle Burn on a footbridge. Continue upstream, going through a Spruce woodland to exit at a stile signposted 'Ovingham $2^1/_2$m'. Just past Narrow Bogle Burn, turn right and cross Whittle Burn on a footbridge. Take the uphill path to **Spital Farm**, going behind it, and taking the road to reach the Harlow Hill to Horsley road. After $^1/_4$ mile, just before the houses of North Dunslaw Holm, turn left along a signposted concrete road. Go through a metal gate on your right and continue along a cart track. Go through a kissing gate and follow a path that skirts Horsley Hill. Descend to cross the A69 and turn right along a walled path for $^1/_4$ mile to reach Horsley. Go left, through the village, to reach a road sign for 'Horsley Wood Cottages $^1/_2$m'. Turn right at the Methodist Church and go along Mill Lane for $^1/_2$ mile, passing the cottages to enter Horsley Wood. Bear left at a crossing of tracks, going along a rutted track to reach the Wylam to Ovingham road opposite a pumping station. Turn left, along the road, but where it curves left, away from the Tyne, keep straight ahead along a stepped path on the riverside to reach Hagg Bank Bridge. Cross and bear right, as directed by signposts, to reach Hagg Bank Cottages. There, turn right, along the front street and continue through very pleasant woodland. Stay on the surfaced path for 2 miles, passing Hagg Farm. Continue along the stiled riverside path, going under Ovingham Bridge to return to Low Prudhoe car park.

POINTS OF INTEREST:

Ovingham Church – Thomas Bewick, the Northumbrian artist, wood engraver and naturalist, is buried at St Mary the Virgin's Church.

Spital Farm – its name implies, the farm was once a hospital. Prudhoe Castle, seen towards the end of the walk, was founded by the D'Umfraville family who came with William the Conqueror. It is 12th century and looks it.

REFRESHMENTS:

The Adam and Eve Inn, Low Prudhoe (tel no: 0661 832323).
The Bridge End Inn, Ovingham (tel no: 0661 832219).
The White Swan, Ovingham (tel no: 0661 832304).
The Lion and Lamb, Horsley (tel no: 0661 852952).
The Crown and Anchor, Horsley (tel no: 0661 853105).

Walk 53   **WALLTOWN AND THE LODDAMS**   5m (8km)
Maps: OS Sheets Landranger 87; Pathfinder NY 66/76.
*A splendid walk eastwards alongside Hadrian's Wall to Great
Chesters fort (Aesica), returning along the course of the Vallum.*
Start: At 675662, Walltown car park.

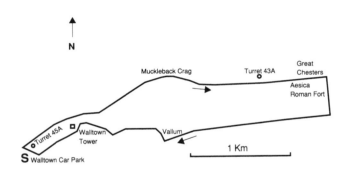

Climb to the Wall and turn right, eastwards, alongside it, following its line behind
Walltown farm. The first Roman construction you pass is Turret 45A, either a signal
station or a forward observation post built during the construction of the wall. The
Nine Nicks of Thirlwall on Walltown Crags are a frequent feature along the Whin
Sill, points of weakness in the rock that were deepened by ice movement during the
last Ice Age to make the depressions seen today. Two of the nine have been swallowed
by Walltown Quarry. Our easy to follow route descends the steep slope from Milecastle
45 to Walltown Nick, climbs to Muckleback Crag, passing Milecastle 44 on the left,
and takes the clear Military Way to **Great Chesters**. Great Chesters was an infantry
fort with gates, towers, underground strong room, granary, administration offices and
shrines. It was built around 128AD. Turn right at the farmhouse and follow the farm

track downhill. Turn right along a surfaced road, going through four gates. After the fourth one the track bends right and crosses the vallum. Continue along it, past Walltown Farm, back to the car park where the walk ends.

POINTS OF INTEREST:

Great Chesters – To the east of Great Chesters a bath house offered hot and cold baths, a steam room, a dry heat room, dressing rooms and latrines. The water supply was carried by aqueduct, one of the most remarkable construction feats of the whole Wall. It was a channel four feet deep and four feet wide which began at the head of Caw Burn, high enough above the camp to allow the water to flow along it naturally. As the crow flies the distance between Burnhead and the bath house was $2\frac{1}{4}$ miles, but to maintain the feed of water the aqueduct took a six miles long winding route. The whole structure was north of the Wall and therefore not protected. The natives, however, were not impressed by personal hygiene, so they left the water supply alone.

Walk 54   **DEBDON ROAD END AND ROTHBURY**   5m (8km)
Maps: OS Sheets Landranger 81; Pathfinder NU 00/01.
Lovely clear paths winding across heather moors and through
pleasing woodland. (Excellent views and no steep hills to climb).
Start: At 067034, Debdon road end, $1^1/_4$ miles north of Rothbury
on the B6341.

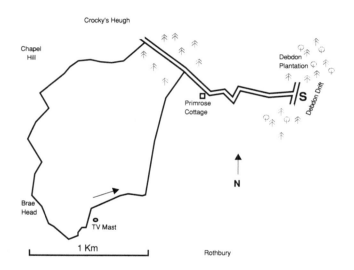

From the road end, opposite the northern end to Cragside, go along the road, westwards,
through a gate. Go left, downhill, and over a little bridge to Primrose Cottage. Turn
right, off the road, at the cottage. Go through a gate and continue alongside a plantation
on your left, following a clear track. Where the track curves left go through a gate and
at a crossing of tracks continue in the same direction. The track goes through a wood
and leads to open moorland: stay on it as it curves left, below the summit of a hill and
then skirts another summit which is topped by a trig point. Continue along the track,
which is now curving eastwards, and at a split of tracks go left, soon to pass the tall
TV aerial on the right. Just before the track reaches a gate leading into a plantation,
turn left on a narrow path, downhill, across heather moor to reach a gate. Go through

and continue in the same direction to reach a stile after $^1/_4$ mile. Go over into a plantation. Continue along a clear path to reach a forest track and turn right, along it, to reach a stile and a T-junction. Turn right, back to Primrose Cottage and from there retrace your steps to the Debdon road end.

POINTS OF INTEREST:
The walk goes through land that was once part of the large Cragside estate. The Armstrong family laid out the clear tracks as carriage drives. Cragside House and its immediate grounds now belong to the National Trust but the land through which this walk goes still belongs to Lord Armstrong.

REFRESHMENTS:
The Queen's Head, Rothbury (tel no: 0669 20470).

Walk 55 **ELSDONBURN AND THE SCOTTISH BORDER**   5m (8km)
Maps: OS Sheets Landranger 74; Pathfinder NT 82/92.
A superb walk with excellent views of the Scottish Borderlands.
Start: At 882282, wayside parking near Hethpool.

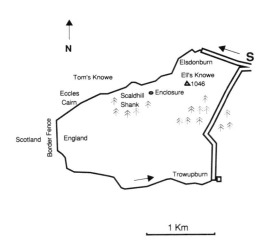

From the grass verge parking area walk along the road for about $\frac{1}{4}$ mile to the farm seen ahead. Go left along a track to the farmyard and cross it, leaving through a gate on the right. Follow a track to the next gate. Just past it go right, along a track to cross a burn. Climb a slope and continue across the field ahead, going diagonally uphill. The farm is Elsdonburn and from it Easter and Wester Tors can be seen. The large enclosure on the left before a plantation is reached is probably Romano-British. Turn right at the plantation and walk to its lower edge. There, go through a gate and turn left, keeping above the burn on your right. At the end of the plantation turn right and cross the burn on planks. Now bear left, up the slope ahead and continue towards **Eccles Cairn**. On reaching level ground just below the summit bear left and go round the cairn.

Continue westwards to a gate in the border fence, but do not go through it. Instead, turn left and follow the border fence to the next gate in it. Now turn left along a path above the burn head to the left, and continue along the middle slopes of the hill on your left. Walk alongside a large walled enclosure on your left to reach Trowupburn Farm. Follow the farm road, passing buildings on your right, all the way back to the start of the walk.

POINTS OF INTEREST:

Eccles Cairn – The cairn is the burial place of a chieftain. It lies close to the border between England and Scotland: below it, westwards, on the Scottish side of the border is Green Humbleton, surrounded by the ramparts and ditches of a pre-historic encampment.

Kirk Yetholm is close to the Scottish-English border, beyond Green Humbleton. It was once the headquarters of the Faa gypsies who pastured their horses near the border fence. In 1883 the last 'Queen of the Gypsies' died there and a small house in the town is called 'The Gypsy Palace'.

Walk 56   **WALLTOWN AND GREENHEAD**   5m (8km)

Maps: OS Sheets Landranger 86; Pathfinder NY 66/76.

An outward walk along the Pennine Way, with the return across lowland fields and upland bogs.

Start: At 675662, Walltown Car Park.

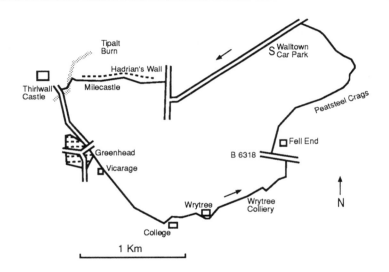

From the car park go westwards along the road to a junction opposite Carvoran Museum, and turn right for 200 yards to reach a stile into a field on the left. Follow the line of the wall and ditch, along the Pennine Way. Cross the field to a stile and continue downhill along the line of a fighting ditch, passing ruinous Milecastle 46 to reach some beeches. Cross a stile and descend to Tipalt Burn. Cross a footbridge at Dooven Foot and turn left at the end of some cottages to follow a track between the edge of the field and Tipalt Burn. Cross a footbridge and turn left over a stile. Follow a footpath between the railway and the burn into Greenhead. At the end of Station Road turn sharp left, cross a road bridge over Tipalt Burn and immediately turn right on to a footpath signposted 'College'. Follow the path through a wood behind the Vicarage. Leave the wood over a stile and take a track across fields to College Farm, entering it through a gate. Take the surfaced road uphill to Wrytree, and follow it round the farm to **Wrytree Colliery**. Climb a bank to the right of a pylon. Now aim for a plantation and follow the wall on your right to a minor road. Turn right, along it, and after 45 yards cross a stile on the left and go over Painsdale Burn. Follow a wall and go through a gate at the top of the field. Turn left, go through a gate, and cross a track and a stile to reach the B6318. Turn left and after 150 yards enter a field on the right through a gate. Follow the path through a farm gate and bear right between buildings, on the left, and a wall. Go through a gate at the end of the track. Follow waymarker arrows around the end of the Moss, cross the vallum and take the track to Lowtown Farm, leaving by a gate behind the house. Follow a track to a second gate leading to a surfaced road. Turn left and walk past Walltown Farm back to the car park.

POINTS OF INTEREST:

Wrytree Colliery – The colliery is owned by Blenkinsopp Colliers Ltd, it being too small to be profitably run by the National Coal Board. It provides about 600 tons of coal a week for the Stella Power Station near Blaydon.

Walk 57   **INGRAM AND COCHRANE PIKE**   5m (8km)

Maps: OS Sheets Landranger 75; Pathfinder NU 01/11.

Good paths for most of the way, coupled with good views.

Start: At 018163, the car park near the toilets and telephone, just over the first bridge (coming from the east) at Ingram.

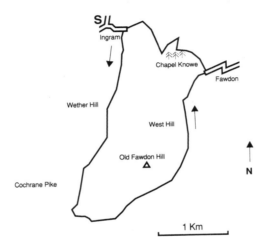

From the car park go along the road past the telephone kiosk, turn left and, where the road bends left, go through a gate on the right signposted Prendwick. Cross the field on rising ground, staying close to the fence on the left. Cross a stile and turn right along a track which soon bears left and goes uphill to a gate. Go through and along a clear track, climbing steadily for $^1/_2$ mile. Where the track splits, go left across an indistinct wet area and then descend along a clear path. During the Border troubles between the late 13th and early 17th centuries this area was ever on the alert. Six men were always on the lookout from 'Prendeke to Engram' to warn of Scottish Reivers rising to plunder the English.

Short of a gate leading to an enclosed field, turn left along a sunken path. Go through a gate, then go left, uphill, on a clear path. At the top turn right and descend along the edge of the bracken towards a facing fence. About 100 yards short of it turn left along an indistinct path, staying close to the fence on your right. The path gradually pulls away from the fence towards a plantation below Old Fawdon Hill on your left. Go to the right of the plantation and a shed, and follow the track at the foot of the steepest slopes of the hill. Continue past another plantation on your right, going along the fence on your right, to reach a stile near a gate. Cross and go diagonally left down a field. Go through a gate and walk towards a tall hedge. On reaching two gates, go through the left one and follow the path beside the hedge on your right. Pass some trees on the left and a cottage at Fawdon, and go through a gate. Go left uphill, passing close to some hilltop trees, to follow a clear track which zig-zags downhill to a gate. Continue on a track through a field, and turn left to reach a road. Go left, retracing your steps to the car park.

POINTS OF INTEREST:

In 1587 some 500 Border Reivers, mostly Armstrong clansmen, swept down from Scotland. They raided Ryle, Prendwick and Ingram, taking 500 cattle, 300 sheep and 20 prisoners. It was one of many such visitations suffered by Ingram.

Walk 58   **MOUNTHOOLY AND THE SCHIL**   5m (8km)

Maps: OS Sheets Landranger 74; Pathfinder NT 82/92.

A superb walk through an area rich in history. A good stretch of it is shared with the Pennine Way.

At 882225, on the grass verge near the gate at Mounthooly.

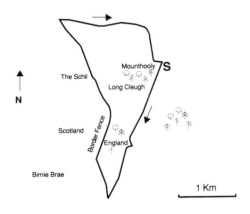

From the gate go along the road, passing a shepherd's bungalow on the left and follow the rack up the valley. The path goes just to the right of the red gash in the hillside ahead, and to the right of a sheepfold. Continue along the lower slopes of the hill on your right, climbing steadily to reach the border fence between England and Scotland. This is the land of the Scottish Marches. Until the Union of the Crowns in 1603 the Border was divided on both sides into the East, Middle and West Marches, each in the charge of a warden who had the almost impossible task of keeping the peace.

Turn right along the border fence, going along the route of the Pennine Way, to reach the summit of The Schil. Descend the other side, go through a gate and continue to a ladder stile. The Pennine Way crosses this stile into Scotland, heading for Kirk Yetholm about six miles away. Our walk turns right at the stile for a few yards, then

122

bears slightly right towards a fence, keeping to the right of rushes which hide the source of the Fleehope Burn. Go through a gate and continue over the rough ground lying to the right of a plantation. Soon a path is reached that passes a sheepfold on the right. Follow the path, which bears right and goes downhill to reach a gate. Turn left to return to Mounthooly.

POINTS OF INTEREST:
The wild Scottish Marches, in the mid-16th century, were in what one Warden called a 'state of decay' due to Scottish raids and, especially, deadly private feuds. The main protagonists were the Armstrongs, Croziers, Elwoods, Erringtons, Fenwicks, Herons, Nixons, Olivers, Shaftoes, Trumbles and Withringtons. By inter-marrying and interminably quarrelling among themselves they created generations of mayhem.

Walk 59 **WOOLER AND WEETWOOD MOOR** 5m (8km)

Maps: OS Sheets Landranger 75; Pathfinder NU 02/12.

A climb to Weetwood Moor with its fine views.

Start: At 994279, the south end of Wooler High Street.

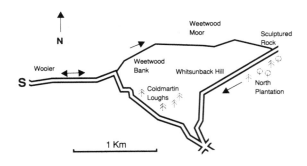

Go down the Perth, cross a bridge and immediately turn left along Brewery Road. The road is named after St Magnus Brewery which was sited on the left, beside a farmhouse. It was demolished in 1960. The cellars are under the farmyard and hops still grow in the hedge opposite. Continue uphill, and where the road curves right, turn left, along a path which leads to a gate. Go through, keep straight ahead for a few yards, and then take a sunken path on the right which, after 150 yards, leads on to the moor. Ignore any sheep trods and follow cairns to reach a stile alongside a gate beside a plantation. A few yards to the left of the path, near a cairn about 150 yards before a road is reached, are the first of several **cup and ring markings** sculptured on stones.

Cross the stile and walk along the fence on your left. Then go along an outcrop of rocks to reach a road through a wicket. **Weetwood Moor's** damp ground and swampy areas attract red grouse and the curlew, Europe's largest wader. Its long, down-curved bill is ideally suited to extracting worms and insects from the moor's marshy pools. Turn right for $1/_4$ mile, and where the road curves left, go straight ahead, along a surfaced track. Follow the track to where it is gated, just beyond a trig point on the right. Go through and continue along the track. Coldmartin Loughs, locally called the Gull Ponds, on the right, are gradually silting up. They are peculiar in that they never completely freeze over, even in the coldest weather. During the winter of 1548/9, some French and German mercenaries garrisoned at Jedburgh with the Scots, found, on a foray into England, that one half was frozen while the other was free of ice.

Stay with the track as it turns sharp right and then reaches a surfaced road. The VHF repeater relay station, passed on the right, was erected for the Post Office in the 1960's. The field to the left of the road as it descends is a favourite haunt of oyster-catchers. Go straight ahead on the road, back into Wooler.

POINTS OF INTEREST:

Cup and ring markings – So called because each consists of a shallow hollow surrounded by concentric circles. They are Bronze Age, dating from about 1600BC. Their meaning is obscure. It is thought they may have had religious significance.

Weetwood Moor – The Moor was once the site of the large annual Whitsunbank Fair. In 1595 a notorious Scottish landowner, Kerr of Cessford, visited it, much to the consternation of the locals. The events leading to this visit were somewhat bizarre. Kerr, feuding with the Storey family had lain in wait between Akeld and Humbleton to ambush and kill any of them on their way to the Fair. The Storeys got wind of this and avoided the ambush. Frustrated, Kerr and his followers abandoned the ambush and all went to the Fair.

REFRESHMENTS:
Hotels, pubs and cafés in Wooler.

Walk 60   ALWINTON AND KIDLANDLEE   5¹/₂m (8.8km)

Maps: OS Sheets Landranger 80; Pathfinder NT 80/90.
*A gentle uphill walk along Clennell Street, an ancient drove road,
and a return along the River Alwin.*
Start: At 919063, Alwinton car park.

Go left for a few yards to a T-junction, cross the village green and a footbridge, and turn left again to go up a track, passing two farm entrances. The track is Clennell Street: follow it uphill, through a gate and past a cottage on the right. Soon a plantation will be seen on the right: continue along the track, go through a gate and bear right, passing Uplaw Knowe on the left. Pass some sheep pens on the left, and on skirting the plantation, go through a gate and up to Wholehope, a ruin whose name is pronounced Woolup.

Go through a gate immediately to the right of the ruin and cross the field to its top right corner. Leave through a wicket and turn right along a track for 50 yards to where a grassy path leads left up a forest ride. Walk with a fence on your right to the fence corner, turn right and within 20 yards turn left. Follow waymarkers across the

126

forest track, bearing left down a minor forest ride to some walled enclosures at **Kidlandlee**. Go through a gate and down a narrow field towards a steel shed. Just before the shed, turn right through a gate, then left through another, to reach a gravel track. Go along the track, through a gate, and on to where the track turns right. Go through a gate and along a grassy path beside some trees on the left to reach another gate. Go down a ride. Where the ride bends left, keep straight ahead along a narrow path. Cross a gravel road and continue in the same direction, past a telegraph pole, to reach another gravel road on the valley floor. Turn right, cross a cattle grid and go through a gate on your left. Go uphill for 50 yards and fork left to follow a track winding above the valley. At the top of the climb the track turns sharply to the right: leave it by going straight ahead along a narrow sheep track, gradually bearing away from the valley on the left. Contour the hillside, cross the top of a sike and go towards a gate on the skyline. Cross a nearby stile and go over the field ahead to a corner. Cross a stile and turn left down Clennell Street to regain the start of the walk.

POINTS OF INTEREST:

Kidlandlee – Built at the turn of the century as a shooting lodge. All of Kidlandlee was a hunting ground for centuries. In 1181 the second Odinell de Umfraville leased the grazing to the Abbot of Newminster Abbey near Morpeth but because it was a hunting ground the monks had to cut off three claws from the forepaws of their dogs to prevent them chasing the Lord's game.

REFRESHMENTS:

The Rose & Thistle Inn, Alwinton (tel no: 0434 220202).

Walk 61 HOLBURN GRANGE AND FAWCET HILL 5¹/₂m (8.8km)

Maps: OS Sheets Landranger 75; Pathfinder NU 03/13

Lots of variety on this pleasant walk through forest, pasture and open moorland.

Start: At 051352, the car park at Holburn Grange, through a gate on the left past a row of cottages.

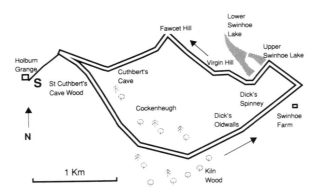

From the car park turn left, through a gate, and along a lane towards Greensheen Hill. At the lane end go through a gate and turn right along a path signposted 'St Cuthberts Cave'. Go through a gate into a plantation and, mid-way through it, take the path to the left which leads to St Cuthbert's Cave. Retrace your route down the hillside. Back on the main path turn left to the end of the plantation and continue along a grassy track between a plantation on the left and arable farmland on the right, bearing right between Cockenheugh and Dancing Green Hill. Go to the end of the forested area, bearing left to a gate. Go through and continue along a track with a wall on your right. The track crosses arable farmland towards another plantation. Go through a gate and along a forest road, crossing Middleton Burn and climbing towards Dick's Oldwalls.

128

Continue to Swinhoe Farm and turn sharp left. The track bears left as it goes alongside Upper and Lower Swinhoe Lakes to the right. Go along a stony track with Virgin Hill to the right, and through a gate on to moorland. Before the next gate, turn three-quarters left, not along the line of the fence, but over the brow of the open moor, aiming for the right-hand side of a fenced square. Go through a gate in the wire fence and downhill to a gate. Go through, cross a drainage channel and follow a straight fence line, aiming for the gap between Cockenheugh on the left and Greensheen on the right. Continue to a gate on the skyline, with a cairn on Greensheen Hill on your right. Bear right along a path through bracken. Sometimes the path is faint, but Holburn Grange is clearly visible and the lane gate can be reached by retracing the route from St Cuthbert's Cave. Once through the gate walk back to the car park.

POINTS OF INTEREST:
Coot and moorhen are numerous on the Swinhoe Lakes, as are the rather noisy mute swans.

Walk 62   ROTHBURY AND GORLEIGH MOOR $5\frac{1}{2}$m (8.8km)

Maps: OS Sheets Landranger 81; Pathfinder NU 00/01.

A nice mix of country roads, fields and moorland give this easy walk variety and interest.

Start: At 051016, Rothbury picnic site, on the B6341 about $\frac{1}{2}$ mile west of the town centre.

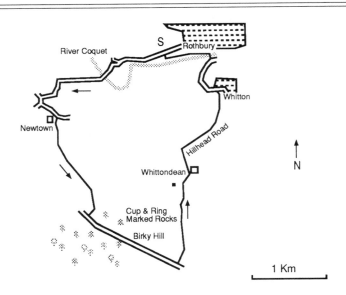

From the car park, go left to a point just past the building on the left, seen on the opposite bank of the River Coquet. There, go through a gate to reach the riverside. As the river bends bear right, away from it to cross some ditches and a stile in the fence ahead. Cross a field diagonally left to reach a footbridge. Cross and follow a path which becomes a farm track leading to houses and a surfaced lane. Go along the lane to a T-junction. Turn left along the road to Newtown. Immediately past East Newton Farmhouse, the last building on the right, turn into the farmyard and at once turn left, through a gate in front of the farmhouse. Cross the field ahead on a track, bearing left to cross Blackburn near two large gateposts. Turn right along a raised bank to a fence, and continue with it on your left to reach a gate. Continue in the same direction, aiming for a line of trees to the left, on the horizon. Pass them on your left, and keep going beside the fence on the left to reach a plantation. Go through a gate, then through another on the right and follow a clear path to a road. Turn left through the plantation and out on to open moor. Turn left at a waymarker about $\frac{1}{4}$ mile short of the plantation ahead.

Cross the moor for a short distance to reach a gate. Bear slightly left along a grassy track near the top of the slope to make a short detour along a path leading left to a large sandstone rock, which has a number of **cup and ring marks**. Return to the grassy track and turn left along it. Do not go to the top of the hill: instead, turn right just before the grassy area ahead, going through bracken to follow a ruinous wall downhill to where a sunken track crosses it at some hawthorn trees. Here turn left to descend to the bottom left-hand corner of a wood near Whittondean. Go through a gate and continue for 50 yards, then turn left, along a track past the front of some cottages. Turn left, as directed by the waymarker, through a garden, and go along a road to a junction. Turn right, along a lane, going past a ruined stone tower. Go left where the lane bifurcates to reach a road junction. Turn right, going downhill and passing a cemetery on the left. Cross a car park, also on the left, and go over a footbridge over the River Coquet. Turn left, upstream and, just beyond the houses above you on the right, go right, up the bank to the picnic site. Turn left, and climb some steps on the right to return to the car park.

POINTS OF INTEREST:
Cup and ring marks – These marks on the rock on Garleigh Moor are Bronze Age and it is thought, because they have also been found in burial sites, that they may have had a religious significance.

REFRESHMENTS:
The Queen's Head, Rothbury (tel no: 0669 20470).

Walk 63   CLENNELL AND PUNCHERTON   5¹/₂m (8.8km)

Maps: OS Sheets Landranger 80; Pathfinder NT 80/90.

A most pleasant walk beside the River Alwin followed by a gentle uphill section.

Start: At 928070, roadside parking close to the unsurfaced road at Clennell.

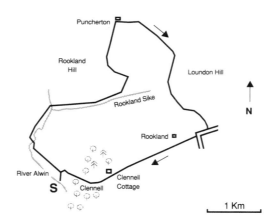

Cross a cattle grid, turn right and continue along the left-hand side of Rookland Sike for about ¹/₂ mile. Go through a gate and bear left, uphill, along a cairned path to reach some ruins, after 300 yards. At Old Rookland, go through a gate on the left and walk to the corner of the ruin. Turn left, along a track towards a gate, then bear right to reach a stile in a fence. Cross and go diagonally right along a cairned way, crossing rough ground. When Puncherton Farm is seen below, descend towards it, crossing a burn to reach a gate between two sikes, one on either side of the farm. Go through the gate and climb the slope with a wall on your right. On reaching a gate turn right, go through the farmyard and continue along the farm track over a field, leaving through a gate. Cross a ford and follow an uphill track, soon going through another gate. Keep on the track, which curves, to reach another gate after $\frac{1}{4}$ mile and, where it bifurcates, go left, through a gate and over a field to a road. Turn right briefly, and where the road turns left, go straight ahead, through a gate and past Rookland House. Continue downhill, along a track, crossing gated fields, to reach a gate, just past a plantation on the right. Go through, pass Clennell Cottage on the right and, 100 yards further on, go through another gate and along a tree lined avenue, passing in front of a house and going through a gate on the right. Turn left, down the road, back to the start.

POINTS OF INTEREST:
The whole area of Kidland is shaped like the spread fingers of a hand, the long, steep ridges being intersected by burns, all of which flow into the River Alwin. The river's name is Old English and means clear water.

REFRESHMENTS:
The nearest is *The Salmon Inn*, Holystone (tel no: 0669 50285).

Walk 64 THE HARTHOPE VALLEY AND BROADSTRUTHER $5^1/_2$m (8.8km)

Maps: OS Sheets Landranger 75; Pathfinder NU 02/12.

No steep climbs, but rough in places and with few landmarks.
Start: At 955227, $^1/_2$ mile beyond Langlee cottage, where there is parking space on the grassy roadside.

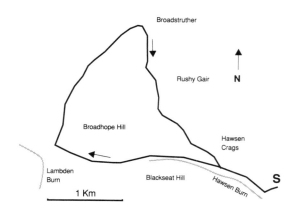

From the roadside parking area, on the left of the road, take the bridleway to the right, signposted 'Broadstruther, Wooler Common'. The path goes uphill and parallel to the road, and turns right just short of a sheepfold to continue above Hawsen Burn. Sheepfolds, called *stells* in Northumberland, are mostly circular structures. Some are divided into several sections and some have projecting walls to provide added shelter. A few are backed against mountain walls. In south-east Scotland the folds are called *bields* and, in west Scotland, *fanks*.

Continue in the same direction, crossing several paths and following the Hawsen Burn upstream. Cross a sike, and where the path bifurcates after 250 yards go left for 500 yards to reach another sheepfold. Continue almost to the head of the burn, and

134

where it curves left to its source, go ahead, bearing slightly right, away from it, up a bracken and grass slope. Cross the flank of Broadhope Hill on the right and go over a stile in a fence. The way ahead involves some difficult route finding, SO IN MIST OR BAD WEATHER RETRACE YOUR STEPS TO THE HARTHOPE VALLEY.

Provided conditions are good, go ahead to a cairn and continue towards the left-hand, lower edge of a plantation seen ahead on the right side of the valley. On reaching it cross a stile beside a wide gate and go along a forest road for about 150 yards to where the road bends. Bear right up a grass track through the plantation to reach a stile in a fence. Cross and walk with a fence on your right, soon crossing it over another stile. Continue along a path with the fence on your left until a stream is crossed. Now aim for a cairn seen on the slope ahead, and follow a narrow path around the hillside until, in the distance, the trees at ruinous Broadstruther Farm are seen. Go towards them, and about 100 yards from a facing fence turn right, along a path around the slope. For the next mile follow cairns to reach a gate in a fence. Cross a stile beside it. In a few yards the path below Hawsen Crags, on the left, is reached: follow this back to the outward route and retrace your steps back to the start.

POINTS OF INTEREST:

The Rump of Housey Crag, seen across the valley from above Hawsen Burn has been there for some 380 million years. It was created when the area was subjected to intense volcanic activity which began with outbursts of volcanic violence followed by lava flows over a long period of time.

Walk 65   **STUDDON AND SINDERHOPE**   5$\frac{1}{2}$m (8.8km)

Maps: OS Landranger 87; Pathfinder NY 85/95.

An interesting walk through an area once used by the Bishop of Durham.

Start: At 839538, Studdon crossroads, to the east of Studdon hamlet.

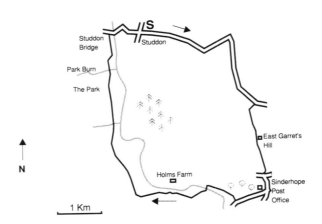

From the crossroads go eastwards, uphill, along a minor road to reach the Allenheads road. Go right, along it, southwards for $\frac{3}{4}$ mile. Where the road bears left you have a splendid view of the Sinderhope valley. Just beyond this bend, at a Sinderhope signpost and where the wall on your right forms a small lay-by, go through a gate. Continue ahead briefly, then turn south, downhill, towards a wall stile. Cross and go through the grove of trees ahead. Go through the farmyard of East Garrets Farm, continuing downhill to reach a wicket in the field corner, near a cottage. Go through to the corner of the main Allendale to Allenheads road. Turn left, cross a stone bridge and turn right on to a minor road. Go along it, briefly, to a footpath sign on your right marked 'Allendale'. Continue through a wicket and along a path with the river on your left, soon reaching the attractive Holms Linn Waterfall. Beyond, cross the river on a wooden bridge and continue with the river on your right. Bear slightly left, uphill, through a wood. Continue westwards, cross a stile into a wood, and go through with care because the ground is boggy. On leaving the wood, bear half-left, briefly, to cross Acton Burn on a wooden bridge. Cross a field and climb some steps up a bank. At a four finger signpost follow the one marked 'Park', soon crossing Cranberry ravine on a plank bridge. Climb the far side, bearing slightly right and coming closer to the river, to reach another ravine. Keep close to a wire fence on your left and descend to cross a wooden bridge, which remains invisible until you are almost upon it. Continue along the riverbank and cross a stile. Pass a farm known as 'Park', cross another bridge and stay on the riverbank to reach a footpath signpost marked 'Sinderhope' pointing back in the direction from which you have come. Here turn sharp right, cross a bridge over the river and climb a zig-zag track to return to Studdon where the walk began.

POINTS OF INTEREST:
Many local farms have the name 'Park' included in their names: Parkgates, Parkside, Wooley Park etc. This is a relic of centuries past when a vast deer forest spread across the dale. Another farmhouse prefix is Hunter: Hunter Oak, Hunter Hill and Hunter Gap are in the Keenley area.

Walk 66 **WOOLER AND FOWBERRY** 6m (9.6km)

Maps: OS Sheets Landranger 75; Pathfinder NT 82/92.

There is a long climb out of Wooler but the views of the Cheviots and Glendale are excellent.

Start: At 994279, the south end of Wooler High Street.

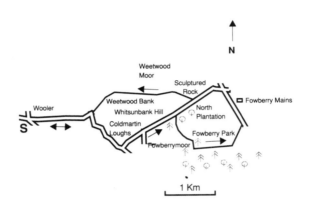

From the High Street go along The Peth, cross a bridge and continue along Brewery Road. Go along a surfaced road that climbs to the top of a hill and continue along an unsurfaced track. Just past the lough and some rough ground on the left, turn left through a wicket and walk to the plantation ahead, keeping a fence on your left. Leave the field through a wicket and walk ahead to reach a farm track. Turn left along the track. Go through a gate and continue along the track. After some 300 yards turn right through a gate marked Fowberry Moor Farm. The fields close to the farmstead on the right are called 'inbye land', and are used at lambing time and for stock the farmer wants to keep under observation. All the other fields are called 'outbye'.

Go along the road until it curves to the farm. There, go through a gate and into a wood. Follow a track as far as a clearing. Turn left and walk to the gate at the plantation edge. Go through the gate and continue straight ahead, crossing a narrow field to reach another gate. Go to the left of the cottage seen ahead, then walk left down the road to reach a crossroads. Turn left. Just past the cattle grid go through a gate on the right and walk past heather to reach a fence. Cross this over a stile near a plantation on the right. Now move away from the plantation, bearing left towards a cairn. Cross the moor and keep straight ahead at the end of some boggy ground on the right to join a green track in the bracken. Continue down the slope, bearing left around the bill. At the bottom of the hill go along a track with the fence on your right to reach a wicket. Go through and follow a somewhat overgrown track to reach a road. Go downhill to return to Wooler.

POINTS OF INTEREST:
About 150 yards from the route on the edge of Weetwood Moor near a stone cairn, there is a large flat rock into which some cup and ring markings have been cut. These obscure markings dated from the Bronze Age.

REFRESHMENTS:
Hotels, pubs and cafés in Wooler.

Walk 67 **HIGH HUMBLETON AND GLEADSCLEUGH** 6m (9.6km)
Maps: OS Sheets Landranger 75; Pathfinder NT 82/92.
Wide views if a clear day is picked.
Start: At 974284, the parking space at the south end of High
Humbleton.

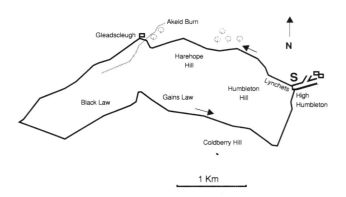

From where the surfaced road ends, go through the gate beside the ruin on the right
and bear slightly right to join a green path by marshy ground. Continue beside the
pond on the right. Follow the path close to the wall on the right and cross a sike to
reach a gate to the left of the wood ahead. Go through a gate and straight up the slope
to another gate. Go through and walk along the lower slopes of Harehope Hill, on the
left. The path leads down the slope to reach a wall on the right. Continue alongside
the wall and, as it turns sharp right, downhill, stay with it and go through a gate. Bear
left near the bottom of the slope. Bridge a burn and go up the slope on the left. Turn
left on to a farm track, go through a gate and walk uphill. Beyond the next gate the
path passes a line of trees and an old wall on the right. Continue towards the small
mature wood ahead, pass the fenced corner of a recently planted wood and go through

a gate. Turn left immediately, going alongside the fence on the left, and go through another gate. A gate in a wall can be seen on the skyline: walk over rough ground towards it. Do not go through the gate. Instead, turn left, alongside the wall on the right.

On reaching the junction of the wall with a wire fence, go through a gate and continue to a second gate. The wall is now on your left: where it turns left, go straight ahead, following a clear tractor route near **Black Law** that curves left to reach a fence. Here cross a stile and bear right at a wall to join a clear track which forks right, around the summit of Gains Law on the left. Continue along a clear path that goes gently downhill for a mile. At the bottom of the hill turn left, then go straight ahead, through a gate and continue down a lane back to High Humbleton.

POINTS OF INTEREST:

Black Law – An archeological dig here during the summer of 1980 showed that the circular patches among the heather were the sites of Bronze Age huts. The hill was formed from lava from the Cheviot volcanoes which were active about 380 million years ago. The lava cooled and hardened into a rock called Andesite.

Walk 68   **WYLAM AND NEWBURN BRIDGE**   6m (9.6km)

Maps: OS Sheets Landranger 88; Pathfinder NZ 06/16.

This easy riverside ramble along both sides of the River Tyne explores the Tyne Valley from Wylam to Newburn Bridge.

Start: Wylam Car Park.

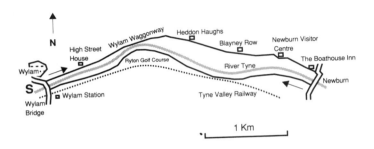

Go eastwards along a bridleway which follows the route of an old railway track called the Wylam Waggon Way, to pass, after $^1/_2$ mile, **High Street House**, then Close House golf course, where you should take care near the fairways. After about 1 mile Heddon Haughs Farm is passed on the left. To the right is the former Heddon Station Master's house. Heddon Station was closed in 1958. As you continue along the disused railway line, the 120 foot spire of the Holy Cross Church of Ryton is seen towering above the trees across the Tyne. About $^1/_2$ mile east of Heddon Station a terrace of cottages, **Blayney Row**, is reached on your left. Continue along a paved footpath on the north side of Grange Road as far as some car park signs. There, cross the road and go left into the Tyne Riverside Country Park at Newburn. From the Visitor Centre in the park cross Leigh Beck on a footbridge and continue along the River Tyne, passing

Newburn Riverside Sports Centre playing fields to reach the Boathouse Inn at West Row. Just beyond, cross the River Tyne on Newburn Bridge and turn right, down steps, to follow a riverside path upstream with the flat grasslands of Ryton Willows on your left. The path goes in front of Ferry House, from where, on your right, the ruinous jetty of the old Ryton Ferry can be seen. Beyond Ferry House the route runs parallel to the Newcastle – Carlisle Railway, then edges Ryton Golf Course. Beyond the Golf Course the route leaves the riverbank and continues along a fenced path beside the railway to exit into Wylam car park.

POINTS OF INTEREST:

High Street House – Better known as Stephenson's Cottage, the house is where George Stephenson 'the father of railways', was born on June 9th, 1781. The cottage, owned by the National Trust, is open to the public.

Blayney Row – The terrace was built in 1889 to house employees of the Isabella Colliery, sited just behind the houses. The mine was opened in 1869 and closed in 1954. The site has now been reclaimed.

REFRESHMENTS:

There are pubs in Wylam.
The Boathouse Inn, West row, Newburn (tel no: 091 267 5150).

Walk 69   **WOOLER AND FOWBERRY MOOR**   6m (9.6km)
Maps: OS Sheets Landranger 75; Pathfinder NU 02/12.
*The long climb out of Wooler offers lovely views of the Cheviots
and Glendale.*
Start: At 991278, the South end of Wooler High Street.

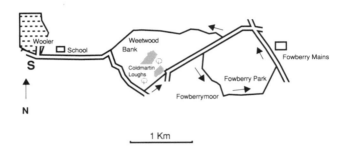

Go down The Perth, cross a bridge and continue along Brewery Road. Follow the
surfaced road that climbs to the top of the hill ahead and go along an unmetalled
track. Just past a lough and some rough ground on the left, turn left through a wicket
in a wall. Continue to the plantation ahead and leave the field by a wicket on to a farm
track. Immediately turn left through a gate, and go along the track for 300 yards. Now
turn right through a gate marked Fowberry Moor Farm. Follow the road until it bears
right to reach the farm, and go straight ahead, through a gate into a wood. Continue
along the track until a clearing is reached. Turn left and go through a gate at the edge
of the plantation. Cross a field to reach another gate, and go to the left of a cottage
seen ahead. The line of hills on the right is the Fell Sandstone Ridge, formed some
300 million years ago when most of the country was covered in large, sandy deltas.

Later faulting and folding caused today's steep, rocky escarpments. The rock, a lovely pink stone, has been used extensively around Edinburgh.

Turn left on reaching the road and go left again at the crossroads. Now, just past a cattle grid, go through a gate on the right and continue up the edge of the heather to cross a stile at a fence beside the plantation on the right. Bear left towards a cairn, going away from the plantation on the right, cross the moor and continue past the boggy ground on the right to join a green track through bracken. Glendale, the valley of the River Glen, which flows into the River Til, lies below. The hollow was formed by a glacier during the Ice Ages and later filled with meltwater to form a large lake which eventually drained away through Etal Gorge some ten miles to the north west.

Continue down the slope, bearing left around the hill. At the bottom, follow the path close to a fence on your right to reach a wicket. Go through and continue down an overgrown track to reach a road. Follow this downhill back to Wooler.

POINTS OF INTEREST:
The beautiful old walls near Fowberry Mains are called dry-stone dykes. The skilled craft of building them was known to Neolithic man and to the people of the early Iron Age.

REFRESHMENTS:
There are hotels, pubs and cafés in Wooler.

Walk 70 SOUTH MIDDLETON AND THREESTONE BURN 6m (9.6km)

Maps: OS Sheets Landranger 75; Pathfinder NU 02/12.

A quiet track, the lower slopes of a hill, a grassy path and the quiet of the Cheviots.

Start: At 997234, the west end of South Middleton.

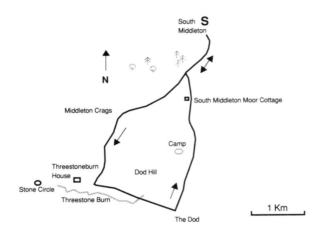

Follow an unsurfaced road south, joining it just below a pond. Take a right fork and walk to the plantation seen on the right. Just past this, go through a gate on the right and then left, in front of a sheepfold, to pick up, in a short distance, a clear and wide farm track which rises gently and runs along the lower slopes of Middleton Crags. The rough moorland below Dod Hill, on the left, is wet and peaty. Here, among the tussocks of purple moor grass, Meadow Pipits nest.

Where the track curves right and goes uphill, keep straight ahead, going through a gate and along an indistinct, sunken, rough path. The path leads to a fence: cross this by stile and continue along a narrow road. The rocky outcrops ahead are Cunyan Crags, from where the land rises to Dunmoor and, beyond, to Hedgehope, the second highest hill in the Cheviot range. Also ahead is the valley of Threestone Burn. In it, just beyond Threestoneburn House and its surround of trees, there is a stone circle which may be Bronze Age. Over the ridge beyond the house, and to the right of Hedgehope, lies Langleeford in the Harthope Valley.

Turn left and walk along the road to The Dod, the farm on the right, and take the path left, opposite the last of the sheep pens. Pass some rocks on the left and continue to cross the burn on a footbridge. Go up the slope to the left corner of a fence and walk alongside it, passing just below a rounded knoll on the right. A few yards to the left of the path is a saucer-shaped enclosure which may be Romano-British.

The top of a plantation can be seen ahead peeping over green slopes: aim for it and soon the cottage of South Middleton Moor will come into view. Cross a burn opposite the cottage, go up a slope and walk just to the right of some buildings. Follow the footpath along a grassy slope to the right of the road, soon joining it near the plantation. Follow the road back to **South Middleton**.

POINTS OF INTEREST:

South Middleton – The village lies on the lower slopes of the eastern Cheviot foothills. Though peaceful now, it once suffered at the hands of the Border Reivers: in 1579 the Warden of the East March reported that the Scots had raided the hamlet and stolen all the horses.

Walk 71   **THE ROTHBURY TERRACES**   6m (9.6km)

Maps: OS Sheets Landranger 81; Pathfinder NU 00/10.

A short, easy route which follows some of the old carriageways of the Cragside estate.

Start: At 056017, the centre of Rothbury where there is ample parking.

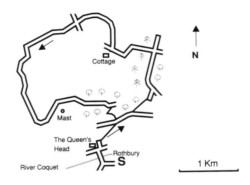

From the centre go eastwards along the B6341, and turn left up a side road, immediately after the Queens Head. Just past the second bend go left up a path between a fence and a hedge. At the top go through a small gate and along a clear path which climbs over three fields to reach a road. Turn right, and just beyond the end of a wood on the left, go left over a ladder stile and along a grassy path which goes half-right up a large field. Cross a stile above a house, and continue climbing to a small gate at the top of a ridge. Continue in the same direction, descending through a wood to reach a road. Turn left, uphill. After $^1/_2$ mile turn left again, down a forest road opposite the entrance to **Cragside.** Follow the road, going through a gate and downhill into a valley to reach a bridge. Cross and continue to a cottage on the left. Go through a gate directly opposite signposted to 'Crocky's Heugh'. Stay with this moor road which soon curves left, round a coniferous wood, and then continues to a gate. Go through, and on, through a second one directly opposite. Continue along a firm moor road for $2^1/_2$ miles, going around a hilltop. Pass a TV mast and go through a gate into a deciduous wood. Follow the path beyond for 600 yards, turning right, off it, to pass an outcrop. Descend steeply through woods, and at the bottom turn left along a facing path. Pass some houses to reach the road used on the outward leg and follow it to return to Rothbury.

POINTS OF INTEREST:

Cragside – In 1863 Sir William Armstrong purchased 20 acres from Archdeacon Thorp and on it he built a two storey lodge. Soon after its completion in 1866 the Armstrongs decided to make Cragside their main residence. Norman Shaw, an architect was commissioned to design a much larger house. Work began in 1870 and the house was completed by 1874. However, further alterations and additions were made until Armstrong's death by which time the house looked much as it does today.

From the Cragside Estate there are extensive views over the Coquet valley to the Simonside Hills, south of Rothbury and, further away, the Cheviots.

REFRESHMENTS:

The Queens Head, Rothbury (tel no: 0669 20470).

Walk 72 **BUDLE BAY** $6^1/_2$m (10.4km)
Maps: OS Sheets Landranger 75; Pathfinder NU 13/23.
A walk that visits superb Bamburgh Castle, the church and the Grace Darling Museum.
Start: At 183349, Bamburgh Castle car park.

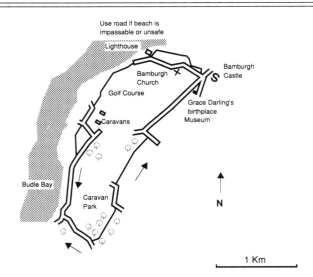

Go back on to the road and turn left. Go around a bend and cross to a footpath signposted 'Lifeboat Cottage $^1/_4$m'. The path goes beside the castle and then turns to the beach. Turn left along the beach for $^2/_3$ mile to reach a lighthouse close to some rocks with a white stag painted on them. Go on to the road and follow it to the entrance to a golf course. Continue along a clear path, passing first a quarry then a wall corner, both on the left. Follow the wall and go through a corner gate on to a surfaced road. Go left, and soon you will reach a gate which, in turn, leads to another road. Go through a small gate and follow a wall up a rough pasture to where it meets a fence. Go through a gate and head half-right across a large field to reach a gate. Go through on to a road and turn right, along it, for $^3/_4$ mile to a road junction. Turn left along a quiet lane, going away from the main road. After $^1/_2$ mile, in a dip in the woods on each side, go left through a small gate and follow a path that climbs half-right. At the top of the climb the path bends left and reaches the edge of a field after about 200 yards.

Continue along the path to a gate and then go half-left to reach another gate leading to a wood. Go through the wood to reach a gate. Beyond, walk in the same direction to another gate into a caravan park. Go through the park, close to its bottom edge, and reach a road through a gate. Turn left to a T-junction. Turn left, and after 650 yards turn right, through a gap. Follow a path running to the left of a fence at the end of which go over the fence in a corner. Continue to the right of a row of trees and cross a stile to the left of a wood. Stay to the left of the wood to reach a stile in a hedge. Go over into a lane and turn left to reach a main road. Turn right and follow the road back to **Bamburgh**.

POINTS OF INTEREST:
Bamburgh – Opposite the church of St Aidan the birthplace of Grace Darling, the local heroine, is marked with a small plaque. Just beyond is the Grace Darling Museum. Grace's sole claim to fame rests on her involvement with the rescue of five survivors of the steamship *Forfarshire* during the early hours of 7 September 1838. She died of tuberculosis on 20 October 1842 at the age of twenty six.

REFRESHMENTS:
Available at Bamburgh.

Walk 73　　　　**ALLEN BANKS**　　　　6$\frac{1}{2}$m (10.4km)

Maps: OS Sheets Landranger 87; Pathfinder NY 66/76 and NY 86/96.

This fine walk follows the River Allen from the confluence of its two tributaries to its meeting with the South Tyne.

Start: At 798641, the National Trust car park near Ridley Hall.

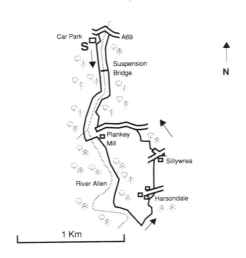

From the far end of the **Allen Banks** car park take the clear path to the riverbank and follow it for $\frac{1}{2}$ mile, ignoring side paths, to reach a suspension bridge. Do not cross: instead, stay on the same side of the river for a further mile to reach Plankey Mill. There cross a second suspension bridge. On the other bank, go right immediately, over a stile, and follow a path through meadows along the left bank of the river. Cross three fields and enter a wood over a stile. Stay beside the river, later moving higher to the left to reach a very clear path that gradually climbs. Where the river bends right, cross a small footbridge and continue alongside a broken wall. Where it ends, regain the river and turn right, using a clear, gently rising path which edges away from the river to reach a stile in a fence on the far side of a wood. Cross the stile and go left, briefly, to a corner. Turn right and cross an open area to reach the far part of the wood, entering over a stile. Follow a path, descending to a bridge and rising to a stile on the far side. Continue to a hedge corner and go right of the hedge to reach a road near Harsondale Farm. Turn right. After 150 yards, where the road bends, cross a stile on the left and go up a field. Cross a stile and turn right to reach another in a fence. Cross and follow the fence round a corner to a wall. Follow the wall down the hillside to Sillywrea Farm. Turn right, along a lane past a barn, turning left after a few yards through double gates into a side lane. At the lane end, cross a field, curving right to reach a gate at the bottom. Go ahead along a field bottom to follow a fence that curves left, around a wood, to reach a lane. Turn left, along the lane to reach the suspension bridge crossed earlier at Plankey Mill. Do not go up to the bridge: instead, turn back half-right, along a rough lane some 100 yards before reaching the Mill. After 50 yards go left, over a stile, and along a path to reach a ladder stile to the left of a ruin. Go over and follow a path to beside the river for $1\frac{1}{2}$ miles to reach a road bridge. Go under the bridge and then right to a gate on to a road. Go right, over the bridge and back to the car park.

POINTS OF INTEREST:

Allen Banks – The 185 acres here, were given to the National Trust by the Honourable Francis Bowes-Lyon in 1942 along with covenants over a larger area of the Ridley Hall Estate nearby.

Walk 74   **ONCE BREWED AND VINDOLANDA**   7m (11.2km)

Maps: OS Sheets Landranger 86; Pathfinder NY 66/76.

A walk in the steps of the Romans that visits Housesteads fort and Vindolanda fort and museum.

Start: At 753668, the Once Brewed Visitor Centre.

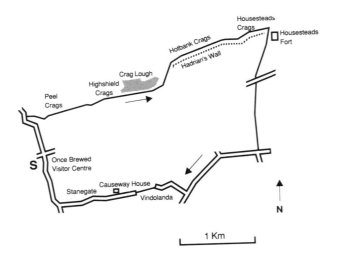

From the car park at Once Brewed turn left, cross the B6318 and continue northwards along a road for ¹/₂ mile. At a sign 'Crag Lough – Housesteads', where the Pennine Way is joined, turn right along the top of the Wall itself for 50 yards, leaving, as requested, down steps. Turn right at the bottom and follow the path for two miles to Housesteads.

The path descends to Peel Gap and ascends Peel Crags on a stone staircase. Stay with the path as it descends into a dip, Sycamore Gap, and climbs to Highshield Crags. The path now descends again, into Rapishaw Gap and then continues most pleasantly along Cuddy's Crags and Housesteads Crags to reach Housesteads Fort, *Vercovium*, perhaps the best known of all the forts along Hadrians Wall.

Turn right at a 19th century well, below the fort, and follow a farm road to the

B6138. Cross the road to a ladder stile. Cross and take a narrow path down a rough pasture to East Crindledikes. Go through the farmyard, following blue markers, and take the farm road to the Stanegate Road. Turn right along the road for a mile. Soon after passing a coach parking area, turn right along a narrow lane to Vindolanda Roman Fort. Continue westwards along the Stanegate Road, passing thatched Causeway House, built in 1775, and at a road junction turn right for the last $^1/_2$ mile back to **Once Brewed**.

POINTS OF INTEREST:

Once Brewed – When Lady Trevelyan opened the Youth Hostel at Once Brewed in 1934, she said she named it the 'Once Brewed', because while it was well-known that ale had to be brewed twice, it was to be hoped that the tea at the hostel would only be brewed once!

REFRESHMENTS:

The Twice Brewed Inn (tel no: 0434 344534) on the B6318, Military Road.
There is a tea room at Vindolanda but you cannot use it without an admission ticket to the museum and gardens.

Walk 75   **ALLENDALE AND CATTON**   7m (11.2km)
Maps: OS Sheets Landranger 87; Pathfinder NY 85/95.
A walk to a fine industrial archaeology site.
Start: At 835558, Allendale market square.

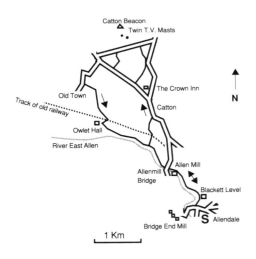

Go along The Peth, the B6295, and turn right at a signpost for 'Allenmill – Oakpool'.
Descend a steep, walled path to the river. Turn right, upstream, passing, after 300 yards,
the remains of a derelict winding house, **Blackett Level**. On reaching Allenmill Bridge
cross the road, pass some cottages and continue upstream along a broad track which
gradually deteriorates into a narrow path. Turn right at Catton Burn, along a lane that
cuts through the embankment of a disused railway. Immediately beyond, turn left
over a stile signposted 'Catton'. Walk parallel to the old railway on your left, cross
Catton Burn on a footbridge and go diagonally right, uphill, aiming for a ladder stile.
Go over and continue to a gate in a field corner. Go through and turn left, through
Catton village. Just before the Crown Inn, bear left, along an uphill road signposted
'Staward'. Just past Hall Acres, on the left, turn right, over a ladder stile, and stay
close to the edge of a rough pasture to reach a waymarked, corner stile. Cross this and

the field ahead to exit through a gate. Go over the next field, leaving over a step stile on to the B6295. Turn left, briefly, and cross a wall stile on the left. Go half-right over a field, cross two stiles and cross the next field to a ladder stile. Cross into Folly Lane. Turn left to reach some cottages and a farm on your left. Turn left between the end cottage and a farm to reach a gate signposted 'Huds Riding'. Cross a field diagonally right to reach a gate in the field corner. Cross the next field to a corner stile. Go right along the next field, past Huds Riding, leaving through double gates on to a road. Turn right. Go left at a T-junction to reach Old Town. Turn left, as directed by footpath sign for 'Allen Mill 1^1/$_2$m', past a cottage and a farm. Go through a metal gate and along a walled lane. Go through another gate on to a surfaced lane. Turn right along the lane, ignoring left and right turns to Catton and Old Town Farm. The descending lane becomes a path: turn right at a facing gate, cross a waymarked stile and continue along the edge of the field, guided by yellow waymarkers. Go through a gate, then left over a disused railway track and past a barn, Owlett Hall. Continue along the field edge and where the fence turns right, turn left, past a solitary ash, to leave the field over a wall stile. Turn right, across the field corner and cross a stile into woodland. Take the clear path to the riverside and turn left to follow the riverside path for 1^1/$_2$ miles. Once over Catton Burn, simply retrace your steps to the start.

POINTS OF INTEREST:
Blackett Level – This was intended to run from Allendale to Allenheads, a distance of 7 miles. Work commenced in 1855 but the project was abandoned in 1869 after only 4^1/$_2$ miles had been completed.

REFRESHMENTS:
The Crown Inn, Catton (tel no: 0434 683447).
There are also hotels, pubs and a café in Allendale Town.

Walk 76   **HUMBLETON BURN AND HELLPATH**   7m (11.2km)

Maps: OS Sheets Landranger 75; Pathfinder NT 82/92.

An enjoyable walk into Cheviot country, not hilly and with fine views.

Start: At 977272, the Humbleton Burn Picnic Place.

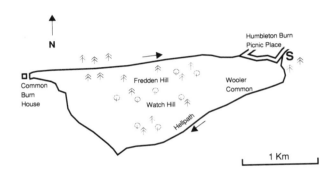

From just before the bridge at the Picnic Place go left, along the footpath beside the burn. Cross a stile and continue along a track which turns left and goes round a low hill on the right. Follow a fence on the left to a gate. Turn right along the road, passing Wooler Common Farm buildings on the right. Go through two more gates and cross the moor. Curlews breed on these upland moors and are frequently heard during the breeding season. The Northumberland National Park has chosen this splendid bird, with its hauntingly beautiful song, as its emblem. Our smallest falcon, the Merlin, hunts this moorland, the fences and stones offering the sort of perches it prefers.

Stay on the path to reach a stile at the edge of a plantation. Cross and follow Hellpath, the name of which is thought to be a corruption of *hill path*, past **Watch Hill**. At the bottom of the path go through a wicket and past a meeting of burns. Cross a

bridge and take the clear path up the slope on the right. Keeping close to a fence on your right, continue above the burn on the left to reach a second gate. Go through, and continue along the path for a further 30 yards. Now turn right for a short distance on rising ground, aiming for a large standing stone: there is a red shed to the right and a low hill to the left of the stone. Go to the left of the hill, bearing left up a farm track. On reaching level ground bear right, through a gate at the foot of some crags. Continue over rough ground heading towards a house. At a facing fence turn right, along it, to reach a stile just before a sheepfold. Cross the stile and continue to Common Burn House. Cross a burn, using a bridge on the right if it is in spate, and go through a gate in the facing wall. Keep ahead, going through a second gate and continuing to a third gate between a cottage and the farmhouse. Turn right at the road and follow it for three miles, back to the picnic place at Humbleton Burn.

POINTS OF INTEREST:

Watch Hill – During the turbulent days of the Border troubles in the 15th and 16th centuries the hill was used as a lookout post. Hence the name.

Walk 77   **STEEL RIGG AND HOUSESTEADS**   7m (11.2km)

Maps: OS Sheets Landranger 86; Pathfinder NY 66.76.

This is the finest section of Hadrian's Wall and the only part
where visitors are allowed to walk along the wall's top.

Start: At 750676, Steel Rigg car park.

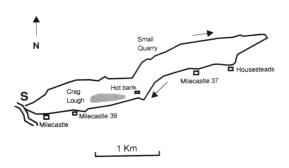

From the car park go on to the road and turn right. At the foot of the hill turn right, along a farm road, and go over a ladder stile signposted 'Hotbank'. Follow the road alongside a wood and cross a ladder stile at its far end. From here the view of Crag Lough is superb. Continue in the same direction along a path close to a wall on the left, passing to the right of a barn. When the wall ends, continue across an open field to a stile. The path now continues to a ditch, bends right, then left, to cross it and crosses a field to reach a stile near gate in a fence. Follow the path across the field ahead, aiming towards the left edge of a hill to the left of a farm. Ignore the path towards the wood: the correct path reaches a stile in a fence. Go over on to a farm road. Go left, briefly, and when the road bends right and fades, keep in the same direction, along a low ridge, ignoring paths going to the left. After a stile is crossed, follow the farm road which goes in the same direction, ignoring the one to the left, indicated by arrows. You are now heading north on the Pennine Way. The farm road soon sinks to a path and goes through a coniferous wood. Follow the path ahead, which descends to the right of a ridge to reach a ladder stile in Hadrian's Wall. Turn right and climb, with the wall on your right, crossing three tops and descending to a ladder stile in a corner. Go through a wood, leaving its far end over a stile, and keep to the left of the Wall as it descends into a valley at Knag Burn Gateway. Climb the far side to Housesteads, and go to the left, following the fort walls to reach the office and museum at the south-west corner. Here you pay if you wish to see the fort and museum. Leave by the West Gate and turn right to the Wall. Climb on to it and go left, along it, until a Milecastle is reached. Descend to the Wall's left-side. Follow the Wall through two dips, climbing to a hilltop and descending to the left near Hotbank Farm. At the bottom the Wall bends to the right: follow it over three ladder stiles to a wood. Go through the wood and continue along the Whin Sill Top to a ladder stile. Descend into a dip and climb some steps to the left of the Wall. Cross a hill to reach another gap and a Milecastle, passing to the right of the castle. Climb some steps to the left of the Wall, cross a hilltop and descend to another stile in another dip. Climb another hill, cross to the right of the Wall to reach a temporary bridge, then go up again, to join the Wall on the opposite side. Stay with it, climbing back to the top and walking along it to reach the road at Steel Rigg and returning to the car park start.

POINTS OF INTEREST:
The Crag Lough and Peel Crag cliffs are frequently used by climbers.

Walk 78   **CRASTER TO BEADNELL HARBOUR**   7m (11.2km)
Maps: OS Sheets Landranger 75 and 81; Pathfinder NU 21/22.
*Part 2 of the Northumbrian Coast Walk. See Walks 84 and 91
for Parts 1 and 3.*
Start: At 256197, Craster Old Quarry car park.

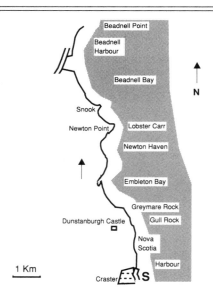

Go on to the road, turn right and follow it to the harbour. Where the main road bears
left out of Craster, a cul-de-sac continues parallel with the coast. Go along it, past a
row of houses on the left, to reach a gate. Go through and follow the coastal path,
heading north. Go through a gate and bear right around a small sandy bay called Nova
Scotia. Stay on the path to Dunstanburgh Castle, and from the Keep bear left, around
the eastern side of Castle Hill. Continue beneath the Lilburn Tower and bear left at
the coast, short of Greymare Rock. Go through a gate and continue north-west, keeping
to the right of a golf course, then following the ridge of dunes into Embleton Bay.
Now follow the high water mark to reach Embleton Burn. Walk left, along it, to a
footbridge. Cross and return to the tideline. Before reaching Newton Seahouses, and
after passing a green hut, take the left-hand path through dunes to join another track.

Turn left past a house and go south for 100 yards to retrace your steps northwards and continue along the track to Newton Seahouses. Go down to the beach and head north-east, crossing a limestone shelf, until you are able to walk along the turf above the rocks. At Newton Point bear left, past Black Kirk Rock, towards Football Hole Bay. From there go north-west towards Snook.

Now go westwards, over a stile and along a dune path leading to a gate close to Newton Links Farm and car park. Turn right to the beach. Go north-west along the upper shore of Beadnell Bay with Newton Links to your left. Do not go near the burn which flows through the dunes: instead, bear left, over a fence at a stile and continue along a path parallel to the burn. Cross the Long Nanny footbridge and go north-east along a track. After 500 yards, at a sign reading 'Coastal Path – Long Nanny Footbridge, Newton Links House' go right, through a wicket, back to the beach to follow the tideline north-east towards Beadnell Point. Walk around it to Beadnell Harbour.

POINTS OF INTEREST:

Gull Crag, north-east of Dunstanburgh Castle, has a seabird colony with fulmars, kittiwakes and guillemots in residence in spring. A favourite roosting place for gulls is the rocks at the southern end of Embleton Bay.

REFRESHMENTS:

There are pubs in most villages along the whole route.

Walk 79   **Rothbury Line and Wannie Line**   7m (11.2km)
Maps: OS Sheets Landranger 81; Pathfinder NZ 08/18.
This National Trust walk is only open to walkers from June to October, to minimise disruption at calving and lambing times.
Start: At 038865, The National Trust car park, Scot's Gap.

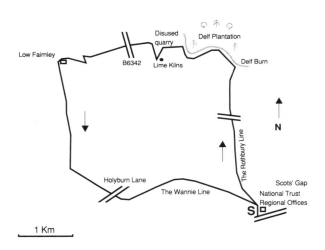

Cross a stile near the NT offices and walk towards a waymarked post. Bear right, cross a sleeper bridge and a stile to reach a disused railway line. Turn left, along it. Where the line bifurcates, go right, along the old **Rothbury Line** for 2 miles. Where the line curves right descend waymarked steps, cross a stile and turn right, then left, along Delf Burn. Cross a stile signposted 'Delf Burn' and turn left into Delf Plantation, keeping close to the burn and following waymarked white posts for $^1/_2$ mile. Climb a steep stepped path and stay close to the plantation's edge, soon leaving it over a stile. Bear right, up a field, to some beech trees on earth dykes faced with walling. Near the top of the field turn right over a stile into another field. Turn left up it, soon descending steps into a quarry. Cross a fence and a stile on your left and follow waymarkers through the abandoned quarry, passing some lime kilns.

On reaching the waymarked corner wall, turn right along the edge of the same field. Turn left down the old quarry road and cross the B6342, the Rothbury Road. Cross a stile opposite, go down a track, cross another stile and bear right along a field boundary. At the end of the field, turn left down the edge of the same field, following waymarkers. Turn right, cross a cattle grid and follow the road ahead to Low Fairnley. Once past it, turn sharp left as directed by a waymarked stone. Pass a pele tower and continue down the field to a bridge over Fairnley Burn. At the end of a plantation on your left cross the field to a waymarked stile in its corner. Beyond, follow waymarked posts, edging stiled fields. Bridge Chesters Burn and aim for a waymarked post near a plantation. Turn right there, over a stile, then go left, along a stiled route. Cross a rough pasture, go over Holy Burn on a slab bridge and aim for a waymarked railway embankment. Turn left, along the old **Wansbeck Line**, returning, after 2 miles, to Scot's Gap.

POINTS OF INTEREST:
Rothbury Line – The line opened in 1870 and was closed in 1963.
Wansbeck Line – The Wannie Line opened in 1865 and was closed in 1966.

Walk 80   **HARTSIDE AND LITTLE DOD**   7m (11.2km)

Maps: OS Sheets Landranger 75; Pathfinder NT 81/91.

A journey into the remoter parts of the Upper Breamish valley.

Start: At 977162, on the roadside close to a sign to Alnhammoor.

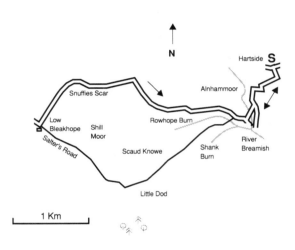

From the sign continue to Hartside Farm, just ahead, and follow the road signposted to Alnhammoor. After about $^1/_2$ mile cross a bridge and continue through a gate. Before the bridge was built there was a ford, then an earlier bridge which was washed away in a severe flood. In July, 1893, a frightful downpour swept away a vast amount of peat from Bloodybush Edge, a hill near the head of the Breamish Valley, and released a tremendous volume of water which washed away all in its path. Pass a barn on your left and cross a cattle grid. After 70 yards go through a gate in the wall on your left. Turn right and go along the wall to reach a fence. Turn left, along the fence, cross a stile and descend to cross Rowhope Burn. Continue, with Shank Burn on your left, for 300 yards to reach a cairn. Keep straight ahead, up the slope, to reach a gate seen in the middle of a fence on the horizon. Go through and follow a path, uphill at first, to pass a sheepfold to the left in almost $^1/_2$ mile. Once past the sheepfold the path becomes less clear: go up a cairned slope and, when the view ahead opens up, aim to the right of the low rounded hill, Little Dod, seen down on the left. At a cairn on a grassy patch alongside Little Dod, bear right and follow the cairned track up and over the ridge to a gate. Go through and walk straight ahead across 300 yards of rough ground. Take the Salter's Road down the valley to a farmhouse. Cross the Hope Sike, turn right in front of the house and follow the road right, uphill, around Snout End. Keep going along the road, passing a small plantation, and soon reaching Alnhammoor house. Now retrace your steps to the start.

POINTS OF INTEREST:
Four-horned Jacob's sheep are frequently seen along the roadside near Hartside Farm. The breed originally came from Palestine.

Walk 81   **BEWICK MOOR AND HAREHOPE** $7^1/_2$m (12km)
Maps: OS Sheets Landranger 75; Pathfinder NU 02/12.
Bewick is a small, rough and lonely wilderness of heather and
bracken covered slopes with occasional rocky outcrops.
Start: At 101244, West of Quarryhouse farm on the Chillingham
to North Charlton road.

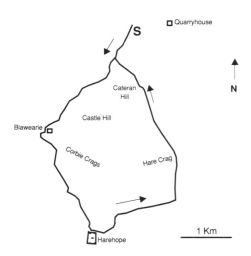

Park near where a wide, green track goes south over the moor. Follow the track, an
old drove road, which carefully avoids wet ground, circling to the left and leading
into a shallow basin with open moorland all round. Soon you cross a small burn and
go through a gate in a fence, the only fence on this part of the moor. Aim for a distant
groove on the skyline, passing a large boulder on the left. Cross a ridge at a track and
turn left to Blawearie. Retrace your steps for 50 yards, and turn left, south, over a
small burn. Bear left around the lower slope of a small hill, aiming for a cairn on the
hill near the remains of a Romano-British camp. Continue along a grassy path, then
bear right on to a ridge between Harehope Burn and Stock Brook. Descend to some
alders on the banks of Harehope Burn. Keep to the right of the burn, go through a gate

168

in the fence ahead and bear left to cross a ruinous wall. Aim for a shallow gap at the foot of Harehope Hill to the right. Cross a stream and walk alongside the fence on your left until Harehope Farm comes into view. When the fence becomes a wall keep alongside it and go through a gate on your left. Continue towards Harehope Farm, which is now on your right. Go through a gate and immediately turn left, near some cottages. Go through another gate into a field. Go left, through another gate and continue beside a fence on your right, still following it when it becomes a wall. Turn left at the end of the field, cross Harehope Burn on a footbridge, go through a gate and rejoin the wall, following it over rough moorland. The path is faint, but runs roughly parallel to the wall, about 15 yards from it. The path skirts the right of a plantation, gaining height and continuing to the right to reach a farm road. Turn left for $1/2$ mile and then go through a gate and bear left, leaving the road. Aim for a distant cairn and pass to the right of Hare Crag. The path is obscure and heather makes hard walking. The ground rises to reach a fence line: go through a gate, past a cairn on the left and on to Cateran Hill. Continue parallel to some crags, keeping to the left of Quarryhouse Moor. Head slightly to the left of a TV mast to reach a green track. Go right, back to the start.

POINTS OF INTEREST:
Beware of rich green patches of ground because the bright colours means there must be a lot of water beneath a layer of Sphagnum moss, the most characteristic of all bog plants. It forms tussocks and complete carpets and holds water like a sponge. Cranberry, sundew, cotton grass and asphodel all grow in these wet places, but heather prefers drier ground.

Walk 82   **CRASTER AND HOWICK HALL**   8m (12.8km)
Maps: OS Sheets Landranger 75 and 81; Pathfinder NU 21/22.
A very attractive walk with much of interest along the way.
Start: At 256197, the car park in the old quarry, Craster.

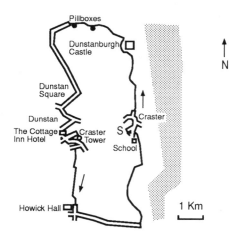

Go on to the road and turn right to the harbour. Take the road left, go through a small
gate and along a green track for $^1/_2$ mile to reach a small gate. Continue for $^1/_4$ mile to
another gate. Keep on the path which slowly climbs to a gate to Dunstanburgh Castle.
From the gate go along the path passing to the left of the castle to reach the shore.
Turn left, away from the castle, along a path parallel to the beach. Stay on the path for
$^3/_4$ mile, staying to the right of a golf course and passing two pillboxes. After the
second one, at a crossing of paths, turn left over a fairway, to reach a farm at a road
end. At the farm, Dunstan Steads, turn left down the lane immediately before the
buildings. Cross the farmyard, go through a gate and along a concrete road for a mile
to reach Dunstan Square Farm. Go through the farmyard and down a road that
immediately bends right. Follow it to a T-junction. Turn left. At the next junction go
ahead to the hamlet of Dunstan. On approaching the Cottage Inn Hotel, go left at a

'Craster Tower' sign along a path that passes in front of cottages to reach a gate. Go half-left across a field to a corner gate leading to a road. Turn right, under an arch, with Craster Tower on you left, and turn left at a crossroads. After the second bend go right, along a rough farm road, signed 'Howick Hall Gates'. Immediately after some cottages go left through a gate and along a path beside a hedge to a stile. Cross and go up a field, bending left with the hedge to reach a ladder stile. Go half-right to a ladder stile in a wall, signposted 'Howick Hall'. Continue slightly left, over a field, to a gate. Follow a broad path, keeping to the right of a field. At a field corner turn right, along a farm road which leads to the entrance gates of **Howick Hall**. Turn left along the road to a T-junction. Continue ahead, through a gate signposted 'Coastal Path Craster', and walk to a gate near the shore. Turn left along a path. The path runs to the right of a road and parallel with the sea. Beyond the road go through a small gate and along a path to the right, above the cliff. At the cliff's end the path curves left: walk parallel to the beach to reach the old school in Craster. There, cross a ladder stile to the right and continue beside the school grounds to a playing field. Turn left to reach a road and go right, along it, to the harbour at Craster. Turn left back to the car park.

POINTS OF INTEREST:

Howick Hall – Built by Sir Henry Grey in 1782. Its extensive and beautiful gardens, best seen in spring when the daffodils are out, are open to the public in the afternoons, from Easter to September. There is a car park at the entrance.

REFRESHMENTS:

The Cottage Inn Hotel, Dunstan (tel no: 066 576658).
There are also numerous places in Craster.

Walk 83   ALWINTON AND SHILLMOOR   8m (12.8km)

Maps: OS Sheets Landranger 80; Pathfinder NT 80/90 and NT 81/91.

A grand route involving some strenuous rough hill walking.
Start: At 919063, Alwinton car park.

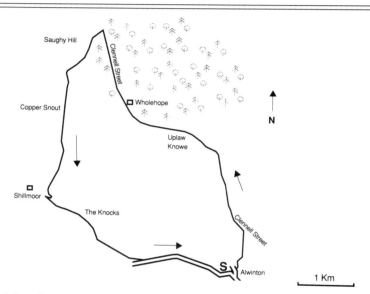

Go left for a few yards to a T-junction. Cross the village green and a footbridge, and go left again to follow a track passing two farm entrances. Go uphill, through a gate and past a cottage on your right. Continue on the track, go through a gate and bear right past Uplaw Knowe on the left. Pass some sheep pens and, on skirting a plantation, go through a gate. Go up the slope to ruinous Wholehope (pronounced Woolup). Continue past the ruin to reach a junction. Go left along a path.

   The path follows the western edge of Kidland Forest: the trees are Norway Spruce. At the end of the forest path go through a gate and continue for about 150 yards to reach a cairn. Turn left across rough grassland going towards the corner of the plantation on your left. Keep a fence on your left, and go through a gate on the left near a sheepfold. The path is faint but it soon becomes clearer: follow it, bearing right over

172

a low hill. When a stony track is joined turn right along it over a hill, almost reaching Shillmoor Farm.

To the right are the Border hills. An old drove road, 'The Street', runs from the Upper Coquet over the hills into Scotland. The long hill in the far distance is Beefstand with Mozie Law to its right. One of the most exposed sections of the Pennine Way runs right along that ridge.

Near the bottom of the hill follow the track round to the left, with Shillmoor Farm below on the right. The track passes a sheepfold on the left and, as Shillmoor is seen again, descends to a wall. Turn sharp left along the wall on the right, and climb a stile. Go on, and cross Wholehope Burn. Stay on the path past The Knocks and above the River Coquet, following it around the hill. Cross two tracks and bear left to cross Passpeth Sike. Here the path bifurcates: take the fork going uphill from the sike to reach a clear, green track that climbs steeply to a dip at the hilltop. At the top of the slope go straight on to cross a farm track and, in $^1/_3$ mile, a sike is reached near a stile at the bottom of a field. Cross and follow a narrow path close to a fence on your left, descending gradually to reach a gate and a stile in a fence. Cross a sike and follow a path downhill for 300 yards to the road. Turn left to reach the start.

POINTS OF INTEREST:

About 100 years ago there was a 'Shepherd's School' at Linbriggs just south of the route. The shepherds would club together and either pay a teacher a fixed salary or offer him 3 pence a week for each scholar. He would live and board with a shepherd as one of the family for a time, then move to another family.

REFRESHMENTS:

The Rose & Thistle Inn, Alwinton (tel no: 0434 220202).

Walk 84   ALNMOUTH TO CRASTER   8m (12.8km)

Map: OS Sheets Landranger 75 and 81; Pathfinder NU 21/22.
No book on walking in Northumberland would be complete without this superb walk along its majestic coastline. This is Part 1 of the route. See Walks 78 and 91 for Parts 2 and 3.
Start: At 246102, Alnmouth Common.

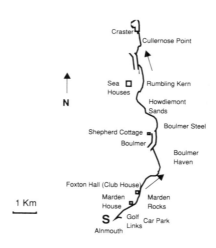

From the Common, beyond the Golf course, walk back for 400 yards to the junction with the main road. Turn sharp right up the steep slope and bear right at the top of the ridge. Continue past the battery where the path opens on to what is the second oldest golf course in England. Keep to the left of the green going along a wall and a fence to reach a cottage. Bear right at a gravelled track but leave it, left, almost at once along a narrow footpath to the beach. Turn left, along the foreshore going north around **Seaton Point**. A footpath cuts across the headland and should be used if the sea is too rough though the best route to follow is just below the sandstone cliffs. Continue round the Point and into Boulmer Haven. There, follow a path along a fence just above the beach to meet a track and bear left with it to a road. Go right into Boulmer.

Turn left at a minor road junction and continue parallel with the coast, passing houses to the right. Go through a gate and walk north to reach a wicket. Go through, over a footbridge and then over a stile on the left. Follow a track north-westwards to a car park above Howdiemont Sands. Go down a path on the right to the beach and continue north around the headland, keeping above a sandstone shelf to reach Sugar Sands. There, go through a gap in the dunes on the left and, just past a lifebuoy, take a footpath sharp left to reach the top path. Turn right along it to descend to a bridge over Howick Burn. Just before a sandstone cliff, turn left, up a sandy path and go through a gate. Go through another gate and along a well-defined coastal path to meet the Craster Road. The track runs parallel to this road before bearing right towards Cullernose Point. There the path climbs on to a ridge. Go through a gate, turn right, keeping to the left of a fence, and cut off the corner of the Point by turning left at a hut. This brings you back to the coastal path: continue north until you are just south of Craster. Now turn sharp left, then bear right to regain the coastline. Keep going northwards to reach a football field. Go left, on to a road and turn right to its end. Turn right immediately, then left, to reach the centre of Craster.

POINTS OF INTEREST:
Seaton Point – Just before the Point, under a field to the left, lies the body of a 53 tonne sperm whale, buried in 1973 after coming aground here.

REFRESHMENTS:
There are pubs in most of the villages along the whole route.

Walk 85   **BLANCHLAND AND SLALEY FOREST**   9m (14.4km)
Maps: OS Sheets Landranger 87; Pathfinder NY 85/95.
This excellent moorland walk offers fine panoramic views and a change of scenery as it nudges and cuts through part of Slaley Forest along an old packhorse trail, the Carrier's Way.
Start: At 962505, Blanchland car park.

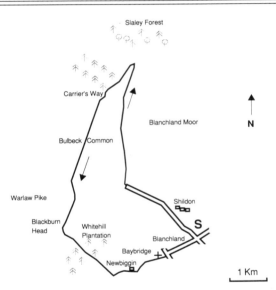

In doubtful weather be well clothed and shod. Map and compass are advised.

From the car park turn left along a surfaced road for ¹/₂ mile, passing Shildon hamlet on the right. Continue along an unsurfaced lane for a further mile to reach **Pennypie House**. Go through a facing gate and follow a moorland track, alongside a wall on the right, across Blanchland Moor, going northwards for 1¹/₂ miles. From this airy, clear bridleway Derwent Reservoir is seen to the east and Pontop Pike TV Mast and Consett are clearly seen on the horizon. Ahead is Slaley Forest: on reaching it, take the first turn left, passing a deep pond, and follow the forest drive through a felled area for a mile. Continue into woodland, and just before the drive curves right, go left, along a narrow path through trees, to leave the forest through a gate on to

Bulbeck Common. Bear half-left, aiming for a fence, and on reaching what looks like a heather covered ditch at a tangent, continue southwards along it. This is the Carrier's Way an old packhorse trail, and is followed for about 2 miles. Go through a gate in a fence. As an added direction guide here, the path goes to the right of the trig point on Warlaw Pike. To the left, on lower ground, are the small pastures of Devil's Water. Pass a tall cairn, go through a gate in a facing wall and keep ahead to reach a fenced enclosure. Continue with the fence on your left to reach a stile. Cross and go to the stone hut just ahead. Go behind it, turn left, through a gate, and follow a broad track eastwards along Reeding Edge. Go through a gate into Whitehill Plantation. Now bear right, following a forest drive downhill and going left along a level drive to exit through a gate. Turn right, close to a wall, and descend the hillside. At the bottom go through a gate and continue down the field ahead to reach a facing bridleway. Turn left, along it, passing Newbiggin Hall, to reach Baybridge hamlet. Turn right, along the road to reach a picnic area on the right. Opposite this go left, along a path signposted to 'Blanchland' following the bank of the River Derwent to finish the walk in fine style.

POINTS OF INTEREST:
Pennypie House – Once an alehouse where pies were sold to miners and drovers for a penny.

REFRESHMENTS:
The Lord Crewe Arms, Blanchland (tel no: 0434 675251).
The White Monk Tearooms, Blanchland.

Walk 86   **KIELDER WATER**   9m (14.4km)

Maps: OS Sheets Landranger 80; Pathfinder NY 68/78.

A walk at the heart of the Kielder Forest.

Start: At 708883, Hawkhope car park at the north end of the
Kielder Water dam.

From the west end of the car park follow a narrow path to a wide forest road. Turn
left, along the road; ignoring all side paths. After $1^1/_2$ miles, the road crosses a bridge
over a river: continue along the road, which soon edges a small lake, to reach the site
of an old village, **Plashetts Colliery Cottages**, now an open area. Stay on the forest
road to a three way junction. Take the middle road, which drops to the left of some
power lines. This is Plashetts Incline Jetty, and the views are simply superb. Turn left
in front of an Information Board and follow a path parallel with the shoreline to reach
Benny Shank Jetty. Orange waymarkers have been placed throughout and footbridges
have been built over feeders where required. Turn left at the picnic tables and go
along the left side of the inlet, crossing to the opposite side when it is safe and
convenient to do so.

178

Turn right down the opposite side of the inlet soon turning left, with the shoreline, into Belling Inlet. When a footbridge is reached which crosses Belling Burn, ignore it and continue alongside the river until a wide bridge and a forest road are reached. This is the bridge crossed on the outward leg and from it the route can be reversed back to the start.

POINTS OF INTEREST:

Plashetts Colliery Cottage – The original mine here was a small drift-mine beside Plashetts Burn, but the opening of a railway line through the valley in 1862 offered the possibility of more intensive commercial development and a local company was granted a lease to work the area of Belling Burn. A small colliery was opened and several cottages were built for the miners and their families. The enterprise proved unprofitable, several companies failing to make it pay, and it ceased operating in the early 1930's.

Walk 87   **BLANCHLAND MOOR**   9¹/₂m (15.2km)

Maps: OS Sheets Landranger 87; Pathfinder NY 85/95 and NY 84/94.

A walk across a grand area of heather moor.

Start: At 965504, Blanchland car park, about 100 yards from the village centre.

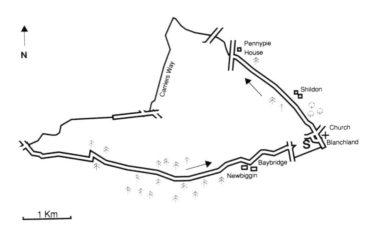

From the car park turn left along the road for ¹/₂ mile to Shildon farm where the surfaced road ends. Continue along the farm road ahead to the next farm, **Pennypie House**. Do not take the farm road to the farm: instead, go through the gate ahead and along a moor road with a small wood on your right. After 100 yards, where the moor road bends, leave it and continue in the same direction up the moor, going to the right of a line of shooting butts to reach a ladder stile in a wall. Cross and go half-left up the moor, crossing its top, Burntshieldhaugh. Go down the far side, briefly, to where a clear path crosses your line of walk. Turn left along it. It is called Carrier's Way, and is an old packhorse trail. It is clearly defined, going through a hollow and contouring the moor. Pass a hut, and then cross a wall through a gate. When a fence is reached, continue with it on your left. Go under some electricity cables to reach a stile. Cross and go half-left to a stone hut, beyond which a wide moor road is reached. Turn right, and follow it until it disappears. Continue in the same direction contouring over pathless moor, and resisting the temptation to descend the slope towards a wood. After $^1/_4$ mile you reach the edge of a wide valley where it bends. Go to the right of a shelf seen slanting down the left-hand side of the central spur of the bend, to reach the valley floor and a fence. Cross the fence at a wet area and go to the right of a sheepfold, crossing the valley floor. At the sheepfold curve right, along a clear path leading to the top of the moor. Continue in the same direction across a trackless area, keeping roughly parallel to two woods on the left. After 600 yards a gate is reached at the far left-hand corner of the moor, beside the second wood. Go through it on to a road, and immediately turn left, through a gate, and follow the road to a deserted farm. Pass the farm and continue along the pleasant farm road for 3 miles to where it becomes surfaced at Newbiggin Farm. Continue on the surfaced road for $^1/_2$ mile to reach the main road at Baybridge. Turn right and cross Beldon Burn, entering County Durham. After 70 yards go left through a gate, and along a delightful wooded path to the right of the river. On reaching a road near Blanchland, turn left over the bridge into the village. Go through an arch by the post office and along the road back to the car park.

POINTS OF INTEREST:

Pennypie House – This was once an inn on the drove road that came from the Slaley Forest area to Baybridge. Passing drovers and local mineworkers purchased pies there at a penny each, hence the name.

REFRESHMENTS:

The Lord Crew Arms Hotel, Blanchland (tel no: 0434 675251).
There is also a café in Blanchland.

Walk 88   WYLAM AND GREENSIDE   10m (16km)

Maps: OS Sheets Landranger 88; Pathfinder NZ 06/16.

A pleasant, easy walk on the outskirts of industrial Tyneside.

Start: At 118645, Wylam Old North Station Yard car park.

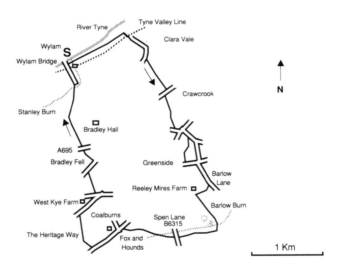

Cross the Tyne on Wylam Bridge and turn left through Wylam Station car park, leaving at its south-east corner. Go along a path parallel to the Tyne Valley railway which soon turns left to follow the riverbank for $^1/_2$ mile to reach Ryton Golf Course. Where the path bifurcates, go right to cross the railway into Clara Vale, a former pit village. Go along the road, which climbs steeply and curves right. Where it levels out, turn left, at a bus stop just before Meadow View, along a signposted, uphill path to reach Crawcrook village. Turn right along Gibson Terrace and, just past a Methodist Church, go left along a signposted path to Meadowfield Park. Go under an arch and along a short path. Go up the edge of a field, cross a road and the next field, leaving over a signed stile. Turn left along Maiden Lane then go left along the B6135 to the Dyke Heads road sign. Now turn right along Folly Lane and go right, along a farm track. At a junction turn left, staying close to the field boundary on your right. At the field's end turn right to cross another field. Turn left, through a gap, at its far end and go along the edge of the next field. Turn right, over a stile and follow a path into Greenside, reaching it opposite the Old School Houses. Turn left, through the village and, almost opposite the Rose and Crown, turn right down Barlow Lane to a footpath sign for Reeley Mires Farm. Go along a track. Pass some cottages and turn right, then left near a derelict building to go along a lane. On reaching a facing gate, turn left along a green lane. Cross a stile and go half-left, past a pylon, to cross a stile on the left. Turn right along a raised path, leaving it over a stile behind holly bushes. Continue to Barlow Burn. Cross a stile, turn right and bridge the burn. Turn right, westwards, along a route marked with yellow arrows and the initials HW (The Hermitage Way), following Barlow Burn. Exit over a stile on to Rougues Lane. Follow a signpost for 'Barlow 1m', walking towards a waymarked telegraph pole beyond a burn. Cross a stile in some holly bushes, turn left and cross four fields to reach a road at Coatburn Cottages. Turn left, and cross a stile on your right signposted for 'Bucks Nook Lane $^1/_2$m'. Cross a field, turn left alongside a wood and, when it ends, continue ahead, past a pylon near a facing gate. Turn right, along a stiled farm track, following a waymarked route to Bucks Nook Lane. Turn right for $^1/_2$ mile to cross a stile on your left. Cut across a field corner into Bradley Fell Road. Turn left almost to West Kygo Farm, but turning right for 'Kygo Bog Lane'. Cross a long field and continue over waymarked fields into Kygo Bog Lane. Turn left past Bradley Fell Farm, go over a bypass and then over the A695.

Walk 89 EAST ALLENDALE AND COWSHILL   10m (16km)
Maps: OS Sheets Landranger 87; Pathfinder NY 84/94.
This scenic walk begins at the best preserved lead mining site in the north Pennines.
Start: At 812433, Kilhope Wheel car park.

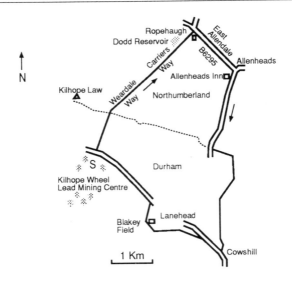

From the car park, ford Kilhope Burn, cross the A689 and enter Weardale forest through a gate marked 'Weardale Estate – PRIVATE'. Go left along a clear track, uphill, and exit the forest over a stile on to Middlehope Moor. Climb northward, staying close to a stream on the left, and crossing tussocky, trackless moor. On reaching an indistinct path, go along it, curving right to reach a green track. This is the Carrier's Way, an ancient highway between Allendale and Weardale. Walk along the Way, heading north-east over Allendale common and passing, after about a mile, the disused Dodd Reservoir on the left. Descend to cross Smelt Mill Bridge over the River East Allen and turn right along the road, soon passing Ropehaugh cottages. Stay with the road in to Allenheads village. Turn right past the Post Office, along the B6295, climbing steadily for 1 mile. At the Northumberland and Durham county boundary fence, turn

184

left through a gate and follow a zig-zag track to cross Kilhope Burn. Turn right, between farm houses, and follow an enclosed track, crossing three meadows and descending diagonally to Heathery Bridge. Do not cross: instead, go left, along a track passing Low Ruch on your left. Continue past Middle Ruch to Blakey Field.

Now go along a track, northwards, to cross Kilhope Burn Bridge. Go diagonally right, along a climbing, green track to reach the A689. Turn left, along the road, for $^1/_2$ mile back to **Kilhope Wheel** car park.

POINTS OF INTEREST:

Kilhope Wheel – The lead mining museum here is well worth a visit. Wheel, Smithy, Stables and Miner's lodgings have all been restored and there are working models and audio-visual displays. England's highest village, Allenheads, is a former lead mining centre.

REFRESHMENTS:

The Allenheads Inn, Allenheads (tel no: 0434 685395).
The Cowshill Hotel, Cowshill (tel no: 0388 537212).
There is also a Craft shop and tearoom in Allenheads.

Walk 90   PAUPERHAUGH BRIDGE TO FELTON   10m (16km)

Maps: OS Sheets Landranger 81; Pathfinder NU 00/10 and NZ 09/19.

The second section of the River Coquet walk.

Start: Pauperhaugh Bridge.

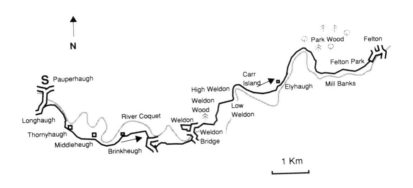

Do not cross the bridge: instead, turn right, along the road, away from the river for $^1/_4$ mile, and cross a stream on the left at a footbridge. Turn left, briefly, cross a stile and keep to the fence on your right, passing Longhaugh Cottage. Turn left, downstream, and at the far end of the field turn right, along a sike, to reach a gate and a bridge. Continue along a track, turn left at a junction and soon turn right through a gate. Cross a field and Maglin Burn, climb the slope and bear slightly left over a field to reach a gate. Continue bearing left over the next field, exiting through a wicket. Go diagonally left over another field to reach a road. Cross to the stile opposite, and turn left, following, firstly, a burn, then a fence around a field to reach the top of a plantation. Go through a wicket and along the fence on your left, above a cliff. Go through a wicket, cross the next field on a path and turn right to Brinkheugh. Go between farm buildings and along a track to a lane. Go along this to a road junction, turn left along a road for 250 yards and, just before a bridge, go through a wall on the left. Follow a track and turn left to reach a white gate. Turn right along a lane, briefly, to enter a field just right of a ruin. Stay with the hedge on your right, going over fields to the footbridge over Tod Burn. Turn left along the Coquet as far as a footbridge and cross to pass the Angler's Arms and reach a road junction. Turn right through an underpass. Walk for 50 yards, then take a road that passes to the left of Low Weldon Farm and goes uphill to High Weldon. Beyond, the track turns right, through a gate, and reaches another gate into a field. Cross the field and leave the track, bearing left through a gate and following an uphill path. Go through another gate on the right and continue above the Coquet, crossing a field. Go over a burn and along the right side of a field, exiting through a wicket. Bear right, past some trees, and cross a stile. Now go along a ridge for $\frac{1}{4}$ mile to a gate. Cross a field to reach a stile, and go over the next field to a gate to the left of Elyhaugh. Cross a track, go through a gate, then go right, past a house for 50 yards, and go through a gate. Walk along the Coquet to reach a footbridge across Swarland Burn. Turn right, briefly, then go left, along a woodland path. On reaching a track, turn right to an underpass. Go through and along a path to a wicket. Go slightly left over a field to reach a wicket on to a road. Go down the hill and turn right at a junction into Felton, the end of the walk.

POINTS OF INTEREST:
Many of the farms passed along this walk end in 'haugh' or 'heugh'. Both names are Old English – 'haugh' means flat land by a stream, and 'heugh' means a projecting ridge which ends abruptly.

REFRESHMENTS:
The Queens Head, Rothbury (tel no: 0669 20470).
The Anglers Arms, Weldon Bridge (tel no: 0665 570655).

187

Walk 91   **BEADNELL HARBOUR TO BUDLE**   10m (16km)
Maps: OS Sheets Landranger 75; Pathfinder NU 21/22.
*Part 3 of the Northumbrian Coast Walk. See Walks 78 and 84
for Parts 1 and 2.*
Start: At 237286, Beadnell Harbour.

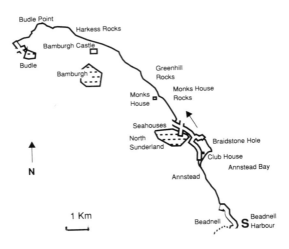

Before starting out on the Coast Walk, take a detour to the left of some kilns which,
with the harbour, are the best bits of Beadnell, and go along the grassy path to Beadnell
Point.

Retrace your steps, then bear right along the boulder-strewn shore for 100 yards
to join the coast road, heading north-west. Keep in the same direction to join the
B1340, the main coast road. On reaching Annstead Burn there is a complication.
When the tide is out the burn is only about an inch deep but at full tide an alternative
route along the road must be used. So, if the tide is out, bear right, along the shoreline,
ford the burn and immediately turn left on to a grassy path which bears right, past
some quarry workings to the left. If the tide is full, go along the right verge of the road
which, after a mile, crosses the burn. About 150 yards further on there is a signposted

path to the right just before a pond. Take this: it is waymarked past a golf club house and then continues east along a ridge. Here both routes converge.

Continue along a clear track, north-west to cut off Snook Point and join a cliff path to the right of a wall. The path bears left into Seahouses and leads to the harbour. Bear left to reach the coast road. Turn right, along it, on its seaward side, from where there are good views of the Farne Islands. Some 300 yards past St Aiden's hotel take the coastal path to the right. Just before a row of houses on the left, turn right down to the beach. Head north-west, along the shoreline to ford Brock Burn, beside **Monks House**. Now head north-west again, along the high tide mark. Cross a limestone shelf and continue along the beach past Islestone Rock, with the coast now turning more westerly towards Bamburgh. Bear to the left of Stag Rock lighthouse and follow the shoreline, using the path at the foot of a grassy bank, above the rocks. This leads to a sandy bay. From there head westward into another bay and continue round the headland to Budle Point. Continue along the upper shore, crossing the dunes at the base of a quay, to rejoin the shoreline. Continue south-west. The beach here becomes shingly, and before the bay broadens out to the left there is a National Nature Reserve sign and a track leading left. Turn left along the track and go past a farm cottage on to the B1342 at Budle.

POINTS OF INTEREST:

Monks House – Monks House Rocks are a good place to watch grey seals. These fascinating creatures, so ungainly ashore, and so graceful in water, breed on the Farne Islands and like to bob close inshore, watching people walking on the beach.

REFRESHMENTS:

There are pubs in most of the villages along the whole route.

Walk 92   **WINDY GYLE**   10$\frac{1}{2}$m (16.8km)

Maps: OS Sheets Landranger 80; Pathfinder NT 81/91.

A superb walk which follows the route of packhorse trains and drovers.

Start: At 860115, near the confluence of the Coquet and Rowhope Burn, about $\frac{1}{2}$ mile upstream of Barrow Burn hamlet.

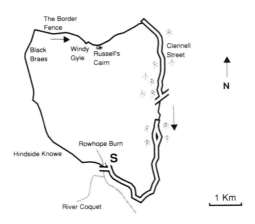

From the parking area cross the bridge and then cross a stile on the right on to a clear path that goes along the spine of a ridge, following a fence on your left. Do not cross this fence: instead, stay to the right of it as it turns right. Some 250 yards past this bend, cross a stile and continue climbing, with the fence now on your right, to reach a gate just below the hilltop. Continue along a path, but fork right after 50 yards, passing the hilltop on the right, and following a descending path to cross a stile beside a notice which reads – KEEP TO THE PATH. UNCLEARED MILITARY TARGET AREA. DO NOT TOUCH ANYTHING, IT MAY EXPLODE AND KILL YOU.

Continue along a clear track, which soon bends left around a small hill, drops to a col and then climbs steeply. Continue climbing to reach the corner of the English-

Scottish Border Fence. Keep in the same direction, with the Fence on your left, ignoring a clear path heading half-right over the moor. At a fence corner do not go through the gate ahead: instead, curve right to follow the Fence. After $1^1/_4$ miles cross the Fence and continue along the Scottish side of it, soon veering away from it, half-left, to reach a cairn which marks the summit of **Windy Gyle**. Return to the Fence and go left, along it for a mile to where it bends half-left, briefly, and joins another fence coming in from the left. Here cross a ladder stile, and leave the Fence along a clear track which descends to reach a gate. Go through and continue along a moor road for $1^1/_4$ miles to reach a rough farm road. Cross this and continue along the path on the spine of the hill ahead. Go over the hilltop and descend to a gate into a forest. Go up the forest road and turn right at the top of the hill, going along a green path that soon bends left, downhill to reach a ladder stile. Cross and go along the moor road ahead for a mile to reach Barrow Burn hamlet. Beyond the first buildings go through a gate and along a farm road. Pass the farm to the right, and continue to a road. Go along the road back to the start.

POINTS OF INTEREST:
Windy Gyle – The huge cairn, Russell's Cairn, on the summit is a Bronze Age mound.

Walk 93   **Derwent Railway** $10^1/_2$m (16.8km)

Maps: OS Sheets Landranger 88; Pathfinder NZ 05/15 and NZ 06/16.

An interesting, all seasons walk along a disused railway line.

Start: At 199620, Swalwell Station Visitor Centre.

Finishing: Blackhill, near Consett.

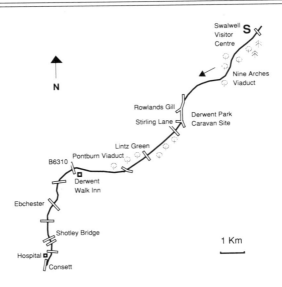

Leave the Visitor Centre along the disused line, going westwards and passing, after $^1/_2$ mile, the site of Derwenthaugh coke works, which is being reclaimed, hopefully to allow the natural beauty of the valley to be extended. Axwell Hall, which overlooks the valley to the north, was built by the Claverings, who were colliery owners. Soon Thornley Wood is passed on the right. It contains a Woodlands Centre which is the starting point for two nature trails. In just over 1 mile a path leads away, left, to Old Hollinside, a 13th century fortified house. The surrounding woodland is part of the Derwent Walk Country Park. As the old line continues up the valley the ruins of Gibside Hall, which was built in 1620, are clearly seen. The nearby 140 feet high monument was built in 1750 to decorate Gibside's grounds. Gibside Chapel, a little

192

further on, has been restored by the National Trust and is open to the public. Lilley brickworks, the site of which is near, and to the north of, Rowlands Gill, was famed for its distinctive off-white bricks, which were made from clay cut from a nearby railway cutting. From the site of the brickworks continue close to the A694, to your right, and where it curves right, go left, briefly, along the B6314. Turn right and cross the railway viaduct over the River Derwent. Continue along the trackbed, passing Friarside chapel on your right, and soon reaching Lintz Green Station, from where an interesting detour leads to Lintzford. From the two viaducts beyond Lintz Green Station there are bird's-eye views of the tree tops in the valley below. Hamsterley viaduct is built of off-white Lilley bricks. Hamsterley Mill, to the north as the line begins to curve towards Ebchester, is a prestigious commuter suburb. About 1 mile beyond Ebchester, Shotley Bridge is reached, beyond which the route passes beneath two more bridges in quick succession. The old line now goes between Shotley Bridge Hospital on the right and a golf course on the left and on to the finish at Blackhill.

POINTS OF INTEREST:

In 1649 a corn mill was built at Lintzford. It became a papermill and, in 1922, an ink works. Lintzford House and the bridge are both 18th century and are attractive.

The bells of Ebchester Church strike the quarter and on special occasions ring out hymn tunes to call parishioners to worship. The church is partly built of second-hand stone from the ramparts of Vindomora, the Roman fort on which Ebchester was based.

REFRESHMENTS:

There is a pub over the bridge and uphill from Ebchester station.

Walk 94   **THE CHEVIOT**   11m (17.6km)

Maps: OS Sheets Landranger 75 and 80; Pathfinder NT 82/92 and NT 81/91.

This route to Scald Hill over Cold Law and Broadhope Hill.

Start: At 959229, near parking notices in Harthopeburn, south-west of Wooler.

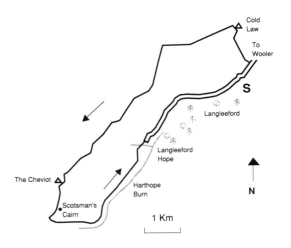

From the parking area go back along the road for $^1/_2$ mile and turn left at a signpost to 'Cold Law'. Go along a green path beside a stream, on the left following wooden waymarker posts. On approaching the top of the ridge go diagonally right, following the posts over the fell to Cold Law summit. From the trig point continue to a fence. Turn left along a clear path to the left of the fence and, at the fence corner, go through a small gate and cross the moor towards Broadhope Hill. From here the views are exceptional.

Return to the small gate and turn right along the fence to reach a stile. Cross, and where the fence turns right, do likewise, to reach the summit of Scald Hill. Cross a stile and continue over rising ground, staying with the fence, to reach the summit of

Cheviot. The summit of Cheviot itself is so boggy you may have trouble finding the trig point; but it is there somewhere, over the fence.

From the trig point continue to walk on the right-hand side of the fence, descending for $^1/_2$ mile and passing a shelter on the other side of the fence. Some 300 yards further on, at a corner where the fence curves left, cross a stile and go diagonally left, keeping to the left of a broken wall. As you descend, the route pulls away from the wall, reaching a stream after about $^1/_2$ mile. Turn left, along the stream's left bank for about $1^3/_4$ miles, going almost as far as a group of trees in front of Langleeford Hope. Just before them, however, cross a stile near a gate at the field corner and walk along the left side of a fence. Where the fence bends right, keep in the same direction to enter a wood. Descend to the right to join a green track and go left, along it, over a ford. Continue to a farm, going to the left of the buildings, to join a farm road. Go along the road for $1^3/_4$ miles back to the parking area.

POINTS OF INTEREST:
An American Flying Fortress crashed on the northwest slope of the Cheviot in 1944. Parts of it are still there.

Walk 95   TOM TALLON'S CRAG   11m (17.6km)

Maps: OS Sheets Landranger 75; Pathfinder NT 82/92.

An easy, low level introduction to the Cheviots.

Start: At 992281, the bus station in High Street, Wooler.

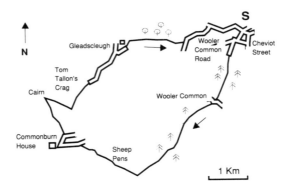

Go left along High Street and bear right along Cheviot Street. Just past a 30mph sign go right, along a footpath, past the Youth Hostel to reach Ramsey's Lane. Turn left and, just before a road junction, go left, up a farm road. Go past a cottage, then right, over a footbridge, and along a bridleway that soon curves right, uphill. Continue towards a forest, turning left where the path bifurcates just short of it. Enter the forest over a stile and continue through it on a clear path, exiting over another stile. Walk beside a fence to reach a farm road through a gate. Turn right past Wooler Common Farm, going through two gates near some sheep pens. Follow a fence to a stile and continue to the corner of a forest. Keep along the forest's right-hand edge, cross a gap and continue along the fence on the left. When it curves left, continue in the same direction, aiming for another forest. Enter this over a stile and follow a clear path that descends towards Carey Burn. Go along the stream to cross a footbridge just past a confluence of streams and at once cross the fence ahead. Follow a path that climbs parallel to the stream on the left, going through two small gates. Turn right along a moorland path at a fence corner, guided by yellow arrows. Once over the ridge ahead aim for the right-hand edge of a facing fence and go through a gate in it, near some sheep pens. Continue along a path, bearing slightly left to reach a fence. Go right, briefly, and then go over a stile in the fence. Keep in the same direction to reach a farm road and go along it to a gate between Commonburn House Farm and a cottage. Go through on to another farm road and turn right, crossing a bridge and going through a gate. Soon, turn left, along a clear track that crosses the moor to reach a cairn where a path comes in from the right. From the cairn double back, half-right, aiming to the right of Tom Tallon's Crag and crossing undefined moor. When a wood comes into view, aim between the crag and the wood to go through a gate in a facing wall. Continue along a path, parallel to a fence, and where a fence from the left meets it at right angles, go left, through a gate, and continue close to the fence on your right. When this turns right, walk ahead, passing to the right of a wood to reach a road. Go along the road to a point immediately before Gleadscleugh, a large house. Now turn right, briefly, and right again. Follow the clear path over a stream and go half-left to reach a gate. Do not go through; instead, go right, uphill, over a stile and at a wall corner turn left, on a clear path which soon leaves the wall and crosses the hillside on the right. Go through a gate in a facing wall and continue past a pond to reach a road. Turn left, then right, through Humbleton. After $1/_4$ mile turn right, through a gate near a seat, and follow the path to the right of a fence. Where it curves right, go through a gate and cross a field to a road. Turn right back to Wooler.

REFRESHMENTS:

There are hotels, pubs and cafés in Wooler.

Walk 96   SALTERS ROAD   12m (19.2km)

Maps: OS Sheets Landranger 80 and 81; Pathfinder NT 81/91.
*This superb walk, apart from the Breamish valley where a
surfaced road is used, is entirely along good clear paths.*
Start: At 996109, the T-junction in the middle of Alnham.

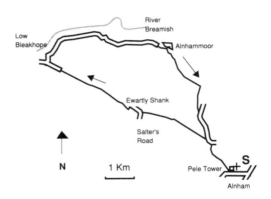

Go up the road signposted 'Alnham Church-Castle Hill-Ewartly', passing the Church
and the **Vicar's Pele**. Where the road bends left, go right, up a lane, through a gate
and along a wallside path. Continue to the top left corner of a field and enter a lane to
the left of a forest. Go to the lane end, then turn half-right to reach a moor road. Turn
left. Where the road goes right, through a gap in a fence, go left, over a stile, and
follow a grassy track to a meeting of a wall and a fence. Keep in the same direction to
reach a sheepfold. Go half-left, up a slope, to the left of a shallow valley to reach a
track. After 125 yards go right at a fork. After 75 yards turn left, along a track, to
reach a gate in a ridge top fence. Descend to the right-hand corner of a wood and
continue alongside it to reach a road. Turn right to Ewartly Shank Farm, passing it as
directed by blue arrows. Beyond, take a path through a wood, leaving through a gate.

Go right, along a track to a stream. Cross, go through a gate and zig-zag up the hill ahead. Descend into a dip, and go out of it again, slanting left to reach a gate on a col. Once through it, descend to the right of a stream along a track that becomes increasingly clear. After a long descent a road is reached at Low Bleakhope. Turn right for $2\frac{1}{2}$ miles, going alongside the lovely Breamish River. On approaching a cattle grid, just before Alnhammoor, cross a stile in a fence on the right and continue left, parallel to the road. Soon you bear right, alongside a wall, to reach a gate. Go through and stay beside the wall, passing a farm to the right and crossing Shankburn where it joins the Breamish River. Cross the footbridge and go over a stile near a gate on to a path which runs parallel to the river on its left. Short of a fence, go right to a gate and up the moor road to a gate and stile at the corner of a wood. Follow the path along the top of the wood, as directed by yellow markers, and cross a stream. Turn right immediately, taking the left bank for $\frac{1}{3}$ mile and gradually pulling away from the stream to reach a moor road. Turn right for $\frac{1}{2}$ mile, then go through a gap in a fence. Continue down the moor road for 300 yards and go half-right across the moor to reach a lane at a corner. Go along the lane to its far end, and continue down a field. Go through a gate and pass a house to reach a road. Turn left back to the T-junction where the walk began.

POINTS OF INTEREST:

Vicar's Pele – Mentioned in 1541, during the Border Troubles. It is said to be haunted.

Walk 97   **THE SCHIL**   14m (22.4km)

Maps: OS Sheets Landranger 74; Pathfinder NT 82/92.

A magnificent ridge walk to The Schil and a return down the valley of College Burn.

Start: At 895283, Hethpool, about 1$^1/_2$ miles along College Valley from Westnewton.

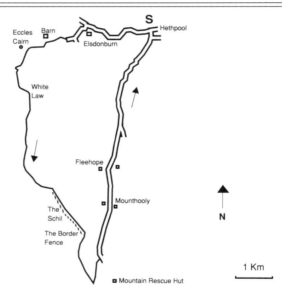

Go north, along the road, briefly, to where it bends right. There, go left along a gated road, bearing right at a junction after a mile and continuing to Elsdon Burn Farm. Just past the house, go right, through a gate, and continue along a farm road. Where this bifurcates, go right, along a farm road that crosses a stream to reach a gate. Go diagonally left across the field ahead and through a gate at the right-hand edge of a plantation. Continue left, round a corner, along a path between the plantation and a stream. Walk in the same direction past the plantation for 200 yards and, just past the point where the stream you are following curves left, turn right and cross it. Bearing slightly left, keep going to the ridge top, ignoring several crossing paths. Here an excellent view will reward a short detour to a hilltop cairn on the right. From the ridge top go diagonally left to reach a gate in a wall, which marks the Border at this point. Turn left, along the wall, to the next gate. Go through and turn left, along a clear path, at first losing height, then climbing to a ladder stile on the top of the ridge. The Border is now marked by a fence. Follow the path to the right of the fence to reach the summit of Whitelaw. Stay with the fence for a further $1\frac{1}{2}$ miles to cross a facing fence over a stile. Now follow a descending path away from the fence. At a signpost turn left to reach a ladder stile. Cross and turn right, along a path that lies to the left of a wall at first, then beside a fence that climbs to the summit of The Schil. Actually the highest point on the rocks is on the opposite side of the fence and a short detour to that high point will reward you with one of the most breathtaking of all the Cheviot views. Retrace your steps to the fence, re-cross it, and continue along it, descending, and bearing to the left. The Border Fence passes close to a **Mountain Rescue Hut**: about 500 yards before it, where the fence bends left, go sharp left, away from it and go over the ridge to join a path to the left of Red Cribs. Follow the path down the left side of the valley, soon reaching a small wood on the left, and a sheepfold and a hut on the right. A moor road starts at the hut: go along it for $4\frac{3}{4}$ miles. The road becomes surfaced, and is followed all the way back to Hethpool.

POINTS OF INTEREST:

Mountain Rescue Hut – The hut seen before you leave the Border Fence replaces a railway wagon. Walkers are requested to leave it in a clean and tidy condition

Walk 98 **THE WEST AND EAST ALLEN'S MEETING** 14m (22.4km)
Maps: OS Sheets Landranger 87; Pathfinder NY 65/75 and
NY 85/95.

*An easy exploration of the very beautiful reaches of the West
and East Allen rivers.*

Start: At 839559, Allendale town centre.

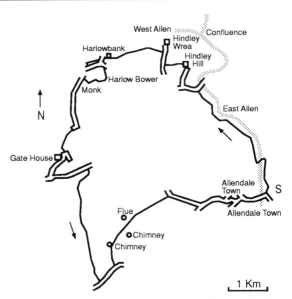

Go along the Whitfield-Haltwhistle road and immediately after it bends left, go right
along a footpath signposted 'Allenmill-Oakpool'. Continue along the river bank for
$^3/_4$ mile to reach a road. Cross the river here and go right along the other bank for $^1/_4$ mile.
Now bear left to reach a gate and continue, briefly, alongside a wall. Go half-left to
re-join the riverbank and stay with it to reach a facing wall. Bear left to a farm road
and go along it, past a farmhouse, over a footbridge and through a wood. Continue
past two more farms, then turn left along an uphill road through a wood. Where the
wood ends turn right, as directed by a 'Hindley Hill – Wide Eals' signpost, along a
minor road. On reaching Hindley Hill Farm turn left, go through a gate and continue

along the left side of a field, going through two gates to reach a lane in front of some farm buildings. Turn right. Just before Hindley Wrea farm go left, through a gate, and along a wall. Where it ends, go diagonally right to a corner gate. Keep straight ahead for $^1/_2$ mile to reach a farm. Pass to the left of it and continue in the same direction to reach a gate to the left of Harlow Bank Farm. Turn right, then left before the house, and go through a gate just beyond a barn. Follow a clear track across the field. Turn left in the middle of the second field, cross a ladder stile on to a road and go left. Soon after passing the road end to Harlow Bank Farm on the right, cross a stile on the right and climb steeply to a gate. Go through and ascend, close to a wall on the right. Cross a stile in a facing wall on to a farm road and turn right to pass Harlow Bower Farm. Go through a gate to the right of a barn and keep ahead to go through another gate. Cross the field ahead to a stile and follow a line of telegraph poles over the next field. At the fifth pole go right, as directed by a waymarker, to reach a gate in a field corner. Go left, as directed by another arrow. Go alongside a fence to reach a gate on to a farm road near Monk Farm. Go left, then right on to track at a fork just short of a cottage. Follow the track through a wood and continue in the same direction to reach a road at Gate House. Go along this for $^1/_2$ mile, then turn left, steeply, uphill. After $^3/_4$ mile, where another road joins from the left, go right, as directed, to 'Dryburn Moor'. The track is clear and curves left into a lane. On leaving the lane continue alongside a wall. Where the wall bends right, keep in the same direction for $^1/_2$ mile to reach a road and turn left along it. Where it bends right, go left through a signposted gate and along a clear track to reach the left of two chimneys seen ahead. Continue alongside the flues, and where they separate, continue to the right of the left-hand one, soon passing a farm and reaching a lane. Turn right at a T-junction, keep straight ahead at a crossroads and turn left at the next T-junction. After $^1/_3$ mile go down a minor road to the right to reach a T-junction. Go left, turn right at a main road, cross a bridge and return to the centre of Allendale Town.

POINTS OF INTEREST:
The two chimneys and flues seen along the walk were built between 1845 and 1850 to serve a smelting mill near the East Allen.

REFRESHMENTS:
There are tearooms in Allendale.

Walk 99   **HOUSESTEADS TO BELLINGHAM**   15m (24km)

Maps: OS Sheets Landranger 80 and 87; Pathfinder NY 88/98, NY 87/97, NY 67/77 and NY 66/76.

Apart from the first mile this route follows the Pennine Way.

Start: At 794684, Housesteads car park.

Finish: At 839834, Bellingham.

Take the path to the fort but do not enter it: instead, go left, to the Wall and turn left along its top to Milecastle 37. Get off the Wall and continue along its left side to Rapishaw Gap. Cross a ladder stile on the right and follow a path signposted 'Pennine Way'. Cross flat moorland to reach a ladder stile and continue in the same direction along a farm road. Cross a ladder stile on a ridge top and follow a descending path to the left, crossing Jenkins Burn and curving right. Go left at a 'Pennine Way' sign, between Greenlee Lough, on the left, and Broomlee Lough. On reaching another PW sign, turn right, briefly, then go half-left. Cross a ladder stile where three walls meet, go over a footbridge and round a wall corner to reach a farm road. Turn right, along it, going into **Wark Forest** for ³/₄ mile. At a PW sign near an open area on the left, leave

204

the road along a footpath. After $^3/_4$ mile leave the forest over a stile. Continue along a clear path over moorland to re-enter the forest, and follow a wide, climbing path to reach a forest road. Turn right, and where the road bends right, keep in the same direction, as directed by PW signs, going over two forest roads to reach a corner where the wall and fence meet. Keep alongside the wall to reach a road. Turn right for 150 yards, then turn left at a PW sign, soon crossing a road and following the path to the end of the forest. Keep in the same direction to reach a stream. Cross and climb to a wall corner. Go to the right of the wall and cross a ladder stile. Go towards Warks Burn, cross a wall on your right and continue to cross a footbridge. Now go half-right to a post. Turn half-left, cross a stile in a fence and another in front of Horneystead Farm. Turn right to a corner where a wall and fence meet and cross two stiles. Pass to the right of the farm head, cross a stile and go along a field to a road near Leadgate Farm. Cross the stile opposite, descend a field to a ladder stile and go half-right to reach Lowstead Farm. Go through the farmyard and turn right along a farm road to reach a T-junction. Turn left, and after $^1/_2$ mile, at the second junction, cross a stile opposite and continue to the left of a fence to reach a footbridge. Turn right to reach a footbridge, cross it and turn left, along a farm road, to reach a fork with a PW sign. Go left, as directed, for 150 yards, then right, through the first gate on the right. Cross the field ahead to a prominent crag and on reaching its top, go directly up the moor and cross a ladder stile. Turn right along a moorland road, soon crossing a stile. Continue for 350 yards, then turn left, at a PW sign, over a moor to reach a road at a bend. Turn left and descend to a T-junction. Go left for a mile to cross the North Tyne, and turn right into Bellingham.

POINTS OF INTEREST:
Wark Forest – Part of the Border Forest Park, established in 1955. It is the largest of Britain's planted forests.

REFRESHMENTS:
The Housesteads Refreshments Bar.
There are hotels, pubs and cafés in Bellingham.

Walk 100　　　　**THE BORDER RIDGE**　　　　$27^1/_2$m (44km)

Maps: OS Sheets Landranger 74 and 80; Pathfinder NT 82/92, NT 61/71 and NT 60/70.

This full traverse of the central ridge is without equal.

Start: At 771023, Byrness church.

Finish: At 827282, Kirk Yetholm.

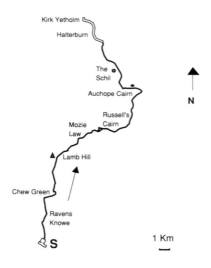

NOTE: This walk is long, there is a lot of climbing along the way and the terrain is tough. These factors make it a route for experienced walkers only.

From the church cross the road and go left, briefly, then right along a path in front of a cottage. Go through a gate with a PW (Pennine Way) sign and walk along a fence. Go through another gate into a forest. Cross a forest road and take the path opposite, crossing another road in a dip and climbing to a small gate at the top of the forest. Go through and climb to the top of Byrness Hill. Turn half-left along the ridge top for 3 miles, keeping parallel to the forest on your left, to reach a stile where 3 fences meet. Continue in the same direction, keeping to the right of a fence until it bends half-left. Here turn right, along a path across moorland. Do not take the path to the left, towards the ridge: instead descend half right to a gate near a stream. Go through it and take a sunken track along the bottom edge of some earthworks. At the far side of them turn left to reach their north-east corner.

Now go right, over a ford and along a clear climbing path. Go through gate and up to a fence corner. From here the fence follows the crest of the ridge all the way to The Schil. This is the Border Fence between England and Scotland. A short diversion to the summit of Cheviot is made at the point where the Border Fence makes a clear cut corner and the path is easy to follow. There is not much to see when you get there, but peak-baggers will enjoy the experience. Return to the Border Fence and stay with it to The Schil. Now descend to a col where a wall starts on the left. Walk along the wall and cross a stile. After a further 250 yards cross a ladder stile to the left and follow a path away from the wall. Where the path splits take the left fork to reach a small gate. Now follow a wide path to the right of a stream, and at a col go right to reach a small gate in a wall, beyond which the path curves across the hillside to reach a fence to the right of a ruin. Finally, follow the road for $2^1/_2$ miles into Kirk Yetholm.

POINTS OF INTEREST:
Small numbers of domestic goats that have become wild exist in the Cheviots on the higher, isolated slopes.

REFRESHMENTS:
Available at Kirk Yetholm.

contents

NZ, Canada, US and UK readers
Please note that Australian cup and spoon
measurements are metric. A conversion chart
appears on page 63.

ingredients from an indonesian kitchen

bok choy, baby also known as pak kat farang, shanghai bok choy, chinese chard or white cabbage; mildly acrid but appealing taste. Available from supermarkets and greengrocers.

banana leaves available from greengrocers. Cut with a sharp knife close to main stem then immerse in hot water so leaves will be pliable.

basmati white, fragrant long-grain rice. It should be washed several times before cooking.

bean sprouts also known as bean shoots; tender new growths of assorted beans and seeds germinated for consumption as sprouts.

bicarbonate of soda also known as baking soda.

capsicum also known as bell pepper or pepper. Discard seeds and membranes before use.

chilli
thai: small, medium hot, and bright red in colour.
sweet chilli sauce: comparatively mild sauce made from red chillies, sugar, garlic and vinegar.

chinese cabbage also known as peking or napa cabbage, wong bok or petsai; elongated shape with pale green, crinkly leaves. Can be eaten raw or braised, steamed or stir-fried.

choy sum also known as pakaukeo or flowering cabbage; has long stems, light green leaves and yellow flowers. Eaten stems and all, it is available at supermarkets and Asian food stores.

cloves dried flower buds of a tropical tree; can be used whole or in ground form.

coconut
cream: obtained commercially from first pressing of coconut flesh, without the addition of water; available in cans and cartons at supermarkets.

desiccated: unsweetened, concentrated, dried, finely shredded coconut.
milk: the diluted liquid from the second pressing of coconut flesh. Available at supermarkets.
shredded: thin strips of dried coconut.

coriander also known as pak chee, cilantro or chinese parsley; bright-green leafy herb with a pungent flavour. Both the stems and roots of coriander are used in cooking; wash well before chopping.

cornflour also known as cornstarch; used as a thickening agent in cooking.

cumin also known as zeera; the dried seed of a plant related to parsley, having a spicy, nutty flavour. Available in seed form or dried and ground from supermarkets.

fennel, seeds available whole and ground; have a strong aniseed flavour.

fish sauce also called nam pla or nuoc nam; made from pulverised, salted fermented fish. Available at supermarkets and Asian food stores.

flour, plain all-purpose flour, made from wheat.

gai larn also known as kanah, gai lum, chinese broccoli and chinese kale; used more for its stems than its coarse leaves.

galangal also known as ka; a rhizome with a hot ginger-citrusy flavour. Sometimes known as thai, siamese or laos ginger, it also comes in a dried powdered form called laos. Fresh ginger can be substituted but the flavour of the dish will differ.

garam masala a blend of spices, originating in North India; based on varying proportions of cardamom, cinnamon, cloves, coriander, fennel and cumin, roasted and ground together.

ghee clarified butter; with the milk solids removed, this fat can be heated to a high temperature without burning.

ginger also known as green or root ginger; thick gnarled root of a tropical plant. Can be kept in a jar in refrigerator, peeled and covered with dry sherry, or frozen in an airtight container.

hokkien noodles also known as stir-fry noodles; fresh wheat noodles resembling thick, yellow-brown spaghetti needing no pre-cooking before being used.

jasmine rice fragrant long-grain rice; white rice can be substituted.

kaffir lime leaves glossy, dark-green, aromatic leaves of a small citrus tree; used fresh or dried

kecap manis a sweet, thick, Indonesian soy sauce. Depending on the brand, the sweetness is derived from either molasses or palm sugar. Available from supermarkets and Asian food stores.

lemon grass a tall, clumping, lemon-smelling and -tasting, sharp-edged grass; the white lower part of the stem is used, finely chopped, in cooking.

macadamia a rich and buttery nut; store in refrigerator because of high oil content.

mustard seeds, black also known as brown mustard seeds; more pungent than white (or yellow) mustard seeds.

oil

peanut: pressed from ground peanuts; used for its high smoke point (capacity to handle high heat without burning).

sesame: made from roasted white sesame seeds; a flavouring rather than cooking medium.

onions

green: also known as scallion or (incorrectly) shallot; immature onion picked before bulb has formed.

red: also known as spanish, red spanish or bermuda onion; a sweet, large, purple-red onion.

spring: crisp, narrow, green-leafed tops and round, sweet, white bulb; larger than green onions.

oyster sauce rich, brown sauce made from oysters, brine, salt, soy sauce and starches.

prawns also known as shrimp.

rice noodles, dried also known as rice stick noodles; made from rice flour and water. Available flat and wide, or very thin (vermicelli). Should be soaked in boiling water to soften.

sambal oelek also ulek or olek; Indonesian in origin. A salty paste made from ground chillies and vinegar.

shrimp, dried also known as goong hang; tiny, salted, sun-dried prawns sold packaged, shelled as a rule, in Asian food stores.

shrimp paste also known as kapi, trasi and blanchan; strong-scented, very firm, preserved paste made of salted dried shrimp. Used as a pungent flavouring, it should be chopped or sliced thinly then wrapped in foil and roasted before use.

spinach also known as english spinach and incorrectly, silverbeet.

sugar

brown: a very soft, fine granulated sugar retaining molasses for its characteristic colour and flavour.

palm: also known as jaggery, or jawa or gula melaka; light-brown to black in colour and usually sold in rock-hard cakes. Brown sugar can be used if unavailable. Purchase from selected supermarkets and Asian food stores.

tamarind concentrate (or paste) commercial result of the distillation of tamarind juice into a condensed, compacted paste. Thick and purple-black, it is ready-to-use, with no soaking or straining required; can be diluted with water according to taste.

tofu also known as bean curd; off-white, custard-like product made from the "milk" of crushed soy beans; comes fresh as soft or firm, and processed as fried or pressed dried sheets. Leftover fresh tofu can be refrigerated in water (which is changed daily) for up to 4 days.

turmeric member of the ginger family; a root that is dried and ground, resulting in the rich yellow powder used in most Asian cuisines. Intensely pungent in taste but not hot. Available from supermarkets and Asian or Indian food stores.

meatball soup

2kg chicken bones
2 medium brown onions (300g), chopped coarsely
2 trimmed sticks celery (150g), chopped coarsely
2 medium carrots (250g), chopped coarsely
4 litres (16 cups) water
1 small white onion (80g), chopped finely
2 cloves garlic, crushed
500g veal mince
2 tablespoons kecap manis
2 tablespoons soy sauce
1 cup (80g) bean sprouts, tips trimmed
4 green onions, sliced thinly

1 Combine bones, brown onion, celery, carrot and the water
in large saucepan; bring to a boil. Reduce heat; simmer, uncovered,
2 hours. Strain through muslin-lined strainer into large bowl.
Reserve stock; discard bones and vegetables.
2 Using hands, combine white onion, garlic, veal, half of the
kecap manis and half of the sauce in large bowl. Roll rounded
teaspoons of veal mixture into balls; place on tray. Cover;
refrigerate 30 minutes.
3 Combine remaining kecap manis and sauce with stock in
large saucepan; bring to a boil. Add meatballs; reduce heat.
Simmer, uncovered, stirring occasionally, about 10 minutes or
until meatballs are cooked through.
4 Divide soup among serving bowls; top with sprouts and
green onion.

serves 6
per serving 2.1g fat; 1016kJ (243 cal)
tip Cook the meatballs in soup close to serving time, to prevent
soup becoming cloudy.

chilli chicken and corn soup

2 tablespoons peanut oil
340g chicken breast fillets
1 medium red onion (170g), chopped finely
1 tablespoon plain flour
1.5 litres (6 cups) chicken stock
2 cups (500ml) tomato juice
420g can corn kernels, drained
2 fresh red thai chillies, seeded, chopped finely
¼ cup loosely packed fresh coriander

1 Heat half of the oil in large saucepan. Cook chicken
until cooked through; when cool enough to handle,
shred into small pieces.
2 Heat remaining oil in pan; cook onion, stirring, until soft.
Add flour; cook, stirring, until mixture bubbles and thickens.
Gradually stir in stock and juice; cook, stirring, until mixture
boils and thickens.
3 Add chicken, corn and chilli; stir over heat until soup is hot.
Just before serving, stir in coriander.

serves 6
per serving 8.5g fat; 1054kJ (252 cal)
tip A purchased barbecued chicken can be substituted for
chicken breasts, if preferred; discard skin, excess fat and
all bones before shredding meat.

garlic and chilli squid

1kg squid hoods
2 teaspoons peanut oil
1 fresh red thai chilli, sliced thinly
chilli paste
2 tablespoons peanut oil
4 cloves garlic, chopped finely
4 fresh red thai chillies, chopped finely
1 tablespoon grated fresh ginger
1 tablespoon white vinegar
1 tablespoon honey

1 Cut squid hoods in half. Score inside surface; cut into
5cm pieces. Combine squid with chilli paste in large bowl.
Cover; refrigerate 3 hours or until required.
2 Drain squid over medium bowl; reserve marinade. Heat oil
in heated large wok; stir-fry squid, in batches, until browned
and tender. Add marinade to wok; bring to a boil. Reduce heat;
simmer, uncovered, until mixture forms a thick glaze. Return
squid to wok; stir through glaze. Serve on shredded green cabbage,
if desired; top with chilli.
chilli paste Blend or process ingredients until almost smooth.

serves 4
per serving 14.5g fat; 1358kJ (325 cal)

lemon grass beef satay

¾ cup (180ml) coconut cream
1 teaspoon crunchy peanut butter
2 teaspoons sambal oelek
2 tablespoons coarsely chopped fresh lemon grass
2 cloves garlic, crushed
1 teaspoon ground coriander
1 teaspoon ground turmeric
750g beef rump steak, cut into 2cm cubes

1 Combine coconut cream, peanut butter, sambal, lemon grass, garlic, coriander and turmeric in large bowl. Add beef to marinade; mix well. Cover; refrigerate several hours or until required.
2 Remove beef from marinade; thread onto 12 bamboo skewers. Grill or barbecue skewers until beef is tender, brushing with marinade during cooking.

makes 12
per serving 6.7g fat; 502kJ (120 cal)
tip Soak the bamboo skewers in water for at least 1 hour before use, to prevent them from scorching.

chilli chicken patties with lime sauce

Any dried rice stick noodle can be crushed for the coating in this recipe; we chose to use a flat, fairly wide bean thread noodle.

50g dried rice noodles, crushed
750g minced chicken
2 teaspoons finely chopped fresh lemon grass
2 teaspoons chopped fresh red thai chilli
1 teaspoon finely grated lime rind
2 tablespoons finely chopped fresh coriander leaves
plain flour
2 tablespoons peanut oil
⅓ cup (80ml) lime juice
2 tablespoons fish sauce
2 tablespoons brown sugar
2 tablespoons rice wine vinegar
⅓ cup (80ml) sweet chilli sauce

1 Place noodles in a small heatproof bowl, cover with boiling water, stand until just tender; drain.
2 Combine noodles with chicken, lemon grass, chilli, rind and half of the coriander in large bowl. Shape ¼ cups of mixture into patties; toss in flour, shake off excess.
3 Heat oil in large pan; cook patties, in batches, until browned both sides and cooked through.
4 Combine remaining ingredients in jar; shake lime sauce well. Serve chicken patties with the lime sauce.

makes 14
per serving 7.2g fat; 556kJ (133 cal)
tip Uncooked chilli chicken patties and the lime sauce can be prepared a day ahead; store separately, covered, in the refrigerator.

gado gado

Gado gado translates roughly as "mixed mixed", which explains the casual way that Indonesians eat this salad. Drizzle vegetables with the sauce and let everyone help themselves. Gado gado can either be served at room temperature or cold.

4 cups (320g) finely shredded
 chinese cabbage
8 baby new potatoes (320g)
2 trimmed corn cobs (500g),
 sliced thickly
200g green beans, halved
1 large carrot (180g),
 sliced thinly
2 lebanese cucumbers (260g),
 sliced diagonally
1 small pineapple (800g),
 chopped coarsely
2 cups (160g) bean sprouts
150g fried tofu,
 chopped coarsely
4 hard-boiled eggs, halved
peanut sauce
1⅓ cups (375g) crunchy
 peanut butter
1 cup (250ml) chicken stock
2 tablespoons light soy sauce
1 tablespoon lemon juice
1 teaspoon sambal oelek
1 clove garlic, crushed
2 teaspoons sugar
½ cup (125ml) coconut milk

1 Boil, steam or microwave cabbage, potatoes, corn, beans and carrot, separately, until vegetables are just tender. Chop potatoes coarsely.

2 Arrange cooked vegetables, cucumber, pineapple, sprouts, tofu and egg on serving platter. Serve gado gado with peanut sauce.

peanut sauce Combine peanut butter, stock, sauce, juice, sambal, garlic and sugar in medium saucepan; bring to a boil. Reduce heat; simmer, stirring, about 1 minute or until sauce thickens slightly. Add coconut milk; stir until hot. Pour sauce into serving bowl.

serves 4
per serving 63.4g fat; 4065kJ (972 cal)
tip We used packaged fried tofu, available from supermarkets. You can, however, shallow-fry cubes of firm tofu in vegetable oil until browned lightly, then drain on absorbent paper, if preferred.
serving suggestion Serve as a light lunch with freshly puffed prawn crackers, or as a more substantial meal with boiled rice and a meat dish.

beef coconut curry

2 tablespoons peanut oil
500g beef rump steak, sliced thinly
1 medium brown onion (150g), sliced thinly
2 teaspoons grated fresh ginger
1 clove garlic, crushed
⅓ cup (100g) mild curry paste
1⅔ cups (400ml) coconut milk
1 medium yellow capsicum (200g), sliced thinly
150g green beans, halved

1 Heat half of the oil in wok; stir-fry beef, in batches, until browned.
2 Heat remaining oil in wok, stir-fry onion until soft. Add ginger, garlic and paste; stir-fry until fragrant.
3 Stir in coconut milk; bring to a boil.
4 Return beef to wok with remaining ingredients; stir-fry until vegetables are tender.

serves 4
per serving 44.2g fat; 2355kJ (563 cal)

mustard-seed chilli prawns

20 large uncooked prawns (1kg)
¼ teaspoon ground turmeric
2 fresh red thai chillies, seeded, chopped finely
2 tablespoons vegetable oil
2 teaspoons black mustard seeds
2 cloves garlic, crushed
2 tablespoons chopped fresh coriander

1 Shell and devein prawns, leaving tails intact. Cut along back of prawn, taking care not to cut all the way through; flatten prawn slightly.
2 Wearing disposable gloves, rub turmeric and chilli into prawns in medium bowl.
3 Heat oil in wok; cook mustard seeds and garlic, stirring, until seeds start to pop. Add prawn mixture; stir-fry until prawns just change colour. Stir in coriander. Serve with green onion curls, if desired.

serves 4
per serving 10.1g fat; 823kJ (197 cal)

crisp beef with gai larn

2 tablespoons cornflour
½ teaspoon bicarbonate of soda
500g beef strips
½ cup (125ml) peanut oil
¼ cup (60ml) sweet chilli sauce
2 tablespoons soy sauce
1 clove garlic, crushed
1 teaspoon sesame oil
1 large red onion (300g), sliced thinly
½ small chinese cabbage (400g), shredded coarsely
400g gai larn, chopped coarsely

1 Combine cornflour and soda in large bowl. Add beef;
toss to coat all over, shaking off excess.
2 Heat a third of the peanut oil in wok; stir-fry about a third of
the beef until crisp. Drain on absorbent paper; cover to keep warm.
Repeat with remaining peanut oil and beef.
3 Combine sauces and garlic in small bowl.
4 Heat sesame oil in same cleaned wok; stir-fry onion until
just tender. Add cabbage and gai larn; stir-fry 1 minute.
Add sauce mixture and beef; stir-fry until heated through.

serves 4
per serving 34.4g fat; 2182kJ (521 cal)

lemon grass chicken

The intense aroma and flavour of lemon grass is an essential ingredient in many Asian dishes. Its widespread appeal means you can find it in most supermarkets but, when slicing or chopping, ensure you use only the white lower section of the stem. Lovely legs are trimmed, skinned chicken drumsticks.

8 chicken lovely legs (960g)
2 tablespoons finely chopped lemon grass
4 spring onions (100g), chopped finely
2 teaspoons fish sauce
1 teaspoon sambal oelek
1 teaspoon sugar
1 tablespoon peanut oil

1 Preheat oven to moderately hot.
2 Combine ingredients in baking dish.
3 Bake, uncovered, in moderately hot oven about 35 minutes or until chicken is cooked through, turning chicken once during cooking.

serves 4
per serving 15.1g fat; 1084kJ (259 cal)
tip You can use any cut of chicken you wish in this recipe.
serving suggestion Coconut rice and steamed chinese broccoli – drizzled with warmed sesame oil and oyster sauce – turn this dish into a satisfying main meal.

chicken curry

This coconut chicken curry is the ideal choice for people who don't like fiery curries.

1 tablespoon peanut oil
750g chicken thigh fillets, chopped coarsely
1 large brown onion (200g), sliced thickly
1 red thai chilli, seeded, chopped finely
2 cloves garlic, crushed
1 tablespoon grated fresh ginger
1 tablespoon finely chopped macadamia nuts
1 tablespoon ground coriander
1 teaspoon ground cumin
½ teaspoon ground fennel
1 cinnamon stick
3¼ cups (800ml) coconut cream
1 tablespoon lemon juice

1 Heat half of the oil in large frying pan; cook chicken, in batches, until browned all over and cooked through.
2 Heat remaining oil in pan; cook onion, chilli, garlic and ginger, stirring, until onion softens. Add nuts and spices; cook, stirring, until fragrant.
3 Return chicken to pan with coconut cream and juice; bring to a boil. Reduce heat; simmer, uncovered, about 5 minutes or until sauce thickens slightly.

serves 4
per serving 62g fat; 3158kJ (755 cal)
serving suggestion This curry is delicious served with steamed rice; garnish with thai chilli slices, if desired.

prawn stir-fry with tamarind

1kg uncooked king prawns, shelled
2 tablespoons vegetable oil
1 clove garlic, crushed
2 teaspoons grated fresh ginger
2 tablespoons finely chopped fresh lemon grass
4 green onions, chopped finely
1 medium red capsicum (200g), sliced thinly
2 tablespoons thick tamarind concentrate
½ cup (125ml) chicken stock
2 teaspoons cornflour
1 tablespoon water

1 Cut almost through backs of prawns; remove dark veins.
Gently press prawns open along cut side with knife.
2 Heat oil in heated large wok; stir-fry garlic, ginger,
lemon grass and onion about 2 minutes or until onion is soft.
Add capsicum and prawns; stir-fry about 2 minutes or
until prawns just change colour.
3 Stir in combined tamarind and stock; stir-fry 1 minute.
Blend cornflour with the water, add to wok; stir-fry until sauce
boils and thickens slightly. Serve over hot noodles, if desired.

serves 4
per serving 10.1g fat; 909kJ (217 cal)

lime and chilli fish baked in banana leaves

2 large banana leaves
4 stalks lemon grass
4 red thai chillies, seeded,
   sliced thinly
4 cloves garlic, crushed
1 tablespoon finely
   grated lime rind
⅓ cup (80ml) lime juice
2 tablespoons grated
   fresh ginger
1 cup loosely packed,
   coarsely chopped
   fresh coriander
1 cup (250ml) light
   coconut milk
8 x 150g firm white fish fillets
cooking-oil spray
2 cups (400g) jasmine rice
4 green onions, sliced thinly

1 Preheat oven to hot (220°C/200°C fan forced).
2 Trim each banana leaf into four 30cm squares. Using metal tongs, dip one square at a time into large saucepan of boiling water; remove immediately. Rinse under cold running water; pat dry with absorbent paper. Banana leaf squares should be soft and pliable.
3 Halve lemon grass stalks lengthways. Combine chilli, garlic, rind, juice, ginger, coriander and coconut milk in small bowl.
4 Centre each fillet on banana leaf square. Top with lemon grass; drizzle with chilli mixture. Fold square over fish to enclose; secure each parcel with kitchen string.
5 Place parcels, in single layer, in large baking dish; coat with cooking-oil spray. Roast in oven about 10 minutes or until fish is cooked as desired.
6 Meanwhile, cook rice, uncovered, in large saucepan of boiling water until tender; drain. Stir onion through rice; serve with unwrapped fish parcels.

serves 8
per serving 7g fat; 1592kJ (381 cal)
serving suggestion Serve this dish with a small side bowl of sweet chilli sauce.

red mullet with peppercorns and lime

4 medium red mullet (1kg)
2 medium limes (160g)
2 tablespoons canned green peppercorns, drained, crushed
1 tablespoon coriander seeds
1 clove garlic, crushed
1 medium red onion (170g), sliced thinly
⅔ cup (160ml) lime juice
⅓ cup (80ml) oyster sauce

1 Score each fish three times on both sides. Using vegetable
peeler, peel rind thinly from limes; cut rind into thin strips.
Rub fish with combined rind, peppercorns, seeds and garlic.
Place fish in shallow dish; top with onion, juice and sauce.
Cover; refrigerate 3 hours, turning once.
2 Remove fish from marinade; reserve marinade. Cook
fish in heated oiled frying pan until cooked as desired,
turning once during cooking. Add reserved marinade
to pan; bring to a boil. Serve over fish.

serves 4
per serving 6.2g fat; 732kJ (175 cal)
serving suggestion Serve on a square of banana leaf with
steamed jasmine rice.

lamb curry with coconut cream

1kg lamb fillets, chopped coarsely
2 tablespoons drained canned green peppercorns, crushed
plain flour
2 tablespoons olive oil
60g ghee
2 green onions, chopped finely
2 cloves garlic, crushed
2 tablespoons finely chopped fresh lemon grass
2 teaspoons coarsely chopped fresh coriander
1 teaspoon grated fresh ginger
¼ teaspoon ground coriander
¼ teaspoon ground cumin
¼ teaspoon ground nutmeg
1 teaspoon grated lemon rind
2 fresh green thai chillies, chopped finely
1⅔ cups (410ml) coconut cream
2 teaspoons sugar
1 teaspoon fish sauce
⅔ cup (100g) unsalted roasted peanuts, chopped coarsely

1 Combine lamb and peppercorns in large bowl; stand 30 minutes.
Toss lamb in flour; shake off excess.
2 Heat oil in large saucepan; cook lamb, in batches, stirring,
over high heat until lamb is well browned all over. Drain on
absorbent paper; discard oil in pan.
3 Melt ghee in pan; cook onion, garlic, lemon grass, fresh coriander,
ginger, spices, rind and chilli, stirring, about 3 minutes or until onion
and chilli are soft. Blend or process mixture until smooth.
4 Return lamb to pan; stir in spice mixture and coconut cream.
Cook, covered, over low heat about 45 minutes or until lamb is tender.
Stir in remaining ingredients. Reheat mixture without boiling.

serves 6
per serving 43.8g fat; 2456kJ (588 cal)
tip This recipe is best made a day ahead; store, covered,
in the refrigerator. It is also suitable to freeze for up to 3 months.

sumatran beef rendang

This famous Sumatran dish is usually simmered for long periods, in rich spices and coconut milk, until the meat is tender and almost dry. We've adjusted the recipe somewhat so you can make it in less than 30 minutes. You will need a piece of ginger about 2cm long to make this recipe.

2 medium brown onions (300g)

2 cloves garlic, quartered

20g piece fresh ginger, peeled

1 tablespoon coarsely chopped lemon grass

1 tablespoon peanut oil

1kg beef fillet, sliced thinly

1 cinnamon stick

2 whole cloves

1 tablespoon ground coriander

1 tablespoon ground cumin

½ cup (45g) desiccated coconut

1 tablespoon tamarind concentrate

¼ cup (60ml) coconut cream

1 Blend or process one quartered onion, garlic, ginger and lemon grass until mixture is almost smooth. Finely chop remaining onion.

2 Heat oil in wok; stir-fry beef and remaining onion, in batches, until beef is browned all over.

3 Add onion mixture to wok with spices and coconut; stir-fry until fragrant.

4 Return beef mixture to wok with tamarind and coconut cream; stir-fry until rendang is almost dry.

serves 4

per serving 27.9g fat; 2132kJ (510 cal)j

tip You can substitute chicken or duck for the beef, if you prefer.
This recipe can be made a day ahead; store, covered, in the refrigerator.

serving suggestion Beef rendang is traditionally eaten with sticky rice cooked in coconut milk, but steamed rice is just as good.

balinese-style lamb

Kecap manis – a sweet, thick, Indonesian soy sauce – is available from all Asian food stores and most large supermarkets. Shrimp paste is often sold as trasi or blachan in Asian food stores, but use it sparingly – a little goes a long way! You will need a piece of ginger about 5cm long for this recipe.

5 fresh red thai chillies, seeded, chopped coarsely
½ teaspoon shrimp paste
2 medium brown onions (300g), chopped coarsely
3 cloves garlic, quartered
50g fresh ginger, peeled, chopped coarsely
2 tablespoons desiccated coconut, toasted
1 tablespoon peanut oil
1kg lamb fillets, sliced thinly
1 tablespoon coarsely grated palm sugar
1 tablespoon kecap manis
1 tablespoon dark soy sauce
1 tablespoon lime juice

1 Blend or process chilli, paste, onion, garlic, ginger and coconut until mixture forms a paste.
2 Heat oil in wok or large frying pan; stir-fry lamb, in batches, until browned all over. Add chilli mixture to wok; stir-fry until fragrant.
3 Return lamb to wok with combined remaining ingredients; stir-fry until heated through.

serves 4
per serving 15.8g fat; 1646kJ (394 cal)
tip Brown or black sugar can be used as a substitute for palm sugar.
serving suggestion Serve with steamed jasmine rice and stir-fried sugar snap peas.

crisp salmon with lemon grass paste

¼ cup (35g) unsalted roasted peanuts
2 fresh red thai chillies, seeded, chopped coarsely
1 stalk fresh lemon grass, chopped coarsely
½ cup tightly packed fresh coriander
⅓ cup (80ml) peanut oil
1 tablespoon lemon juice
2 tablespoons vegetable oil
6 salmon cutlets (1kg)

1 Blend or process nuts, chilli, lemon grass, coriander, peanut oil and juice until mixture forms a paste. Cover paste; refrigerate until required.
2 Heat oil in large frying pan; cook fish, uncovered, until cooked as desired.
3 Serve fish with paste; accompany with roasted potatoes and crisp salad, if desired.

serves 6
per serving 39.4g fat; 2010kJ (481 cal)

eggs in chilli sauce

Sambal goreng telur, as this dish is known throughout Indonesia, is a popular recipe featuring hard-boiled eggs in a rich sauce. The authentic recipe is extremely hot, but you can vary the flavour to suit your tastebuds – use less chilli and more coconut milk for a milder version.

2 teaspoons chilli flakes
1 tablespoon
   coarsely chopped
   macadamia nuts
2 medium brown
   onions (300g),
   chopped coarsely
4 cloves garlic, quartered
2 tablespoons coarsely
   chopped lemon grass
1 tablespoon peanut oil
2 cups (500ml)
   coconut milk
⅔ cup (160ml)
   vegetable stock
1 teaspoon grated
   fresh galangal
4 kaffir lime leaves
8 hard-boiled eggs, halved

1 Blend or process chilli, nuts, onion, garlic, lemon grass and oil until almost smooth.

2 Stir-fry chilli mixture in heated wok until fragrant. Add coconut milk, stock, galangal and lime leaves; bring to a boil. Reduce heat; simmer, stirring, about 5 minutes or until sauce thickens.

3 Add eggs to sauce and cook, uncovered, until hot.

serves 4
per serving 44.5g fat; 2157kJ (516 cal)
tips We used chilli flakes in this recipe but you can use sambal oelek, if you prefer. Eggs can be boiled a day ahead; store, covered, in the refrigerator.
serving suggestion Serve sprinkled with coarsely chopped coriander and steamed jasmine rice.

hokkien mee noodles

600g hokkien noodles
1 tablespoon peanut oil
3 eggs, beaten lightly
500g beef strips
2 cloves garlic, crushed
2cm piece fresh ginger (10g), grated
500g baby bok choy, chopped coarsely
4 green onions, sliced thinly
¼ cup coarsely chopped fresh coriander
2 tablespoons dried shrimp
¼ cup (60ml) kecap manis
2 teaspoons sambal oelek
¼ cup (60ml) beef stock
½ cup (75g) toasted unsalted peanuts

1 Place noodles in large heatproof bowl, cover with
boiling water, separate with fork; drain.
2 Heat a quarter of the oil in wok; cook half of the egg,
tilting pan, until egg mixture is almost set. Remove omelette
from wok; repeat with another quarter of the oil and remaining
egg. Roll omelettes; slice thinly.
3 Heat remaining oil in same wok; stir-fry beef, garlic and ginger,
in batches, until beef is browned all over. Place bok choy in same
wok; stir-fry until just wilted.
4 Return beef mixture to wok with noodles, onion, coriander,
shrimp and combined kecap manis, sambal and stock; stir-fry
until heated through. Serve topped with omelette and peanuts.

serves 4
per serving 24.1g fat; 3350kJ (800 cal)

nasi goreng

Nasi goreng is the Indonesian term for fried rice – easily made using leftover white rice. Shrimp paste, also known as trasi and blachan, is available from Asian food stores and selected supermarkets. You will need to cook about 1½ cups (300g) white long-grain rice for this recipe.

1 small brown onion (100g),chopped coarsely
2 cloves garlic, quartered
1 teaspoon shrimp paste
2 tablespoons peanut oil
4 eggs
125g small shelled uncooked prawns
4 cups (600g) cold, cooked white long-grain rice
3 green onions, sliced thinly
125g Chinese barbecued pork, sliced thinly
2 tablespoons light soy sauce

1 Blend or process brown onion, garlic and paste until almost smooth.
2 Heat half of the oil in medium frying pan; break eggs into pan. Cook, uncovered, until egg white has set and yolk is cooked as desired.
3 Meanwhile, heat remaining oil in wok or large frying pan; stir-fry onion mixture until fragrant. Add prawns; stir-fry until prawns just change colour.
4 Add rice, green onion, pork and sauce; stir-fry until hot. Serve nasi goreng with eggs.

serves 4
per serving 19.9g fat; 1927kJ (461 cal)
tip To save time, freeze single-cup portions of cooked rice and defrost only what you need for each meal.
serving suggestion Serve with a salad such as gado gado, or with prawn crackers and stir-fried Asian greens.

rice noodle and prawn stir-fry

500g medium uncooked prawns
200g dried rice noodles
1 clove garlic, crushed
2 tablespoons soy sauce
2 tablespoons fish sauce
1 teaspoon sambal oelek
1 cup (80g) bean sprouts, tips trimmed
¼ cup fresh coriander

1 Shell and devein prawns, leaving tails intact.
2 Place noodles in large heatproof bowl; cover with boiling water. Stand until just tender; drain. Cover to keep warm.
3 Stir-fry prawns and garlic in heated oiled large wok until prawns just change colour. Add noodles, sauces and sambal; gently stir-fry until hot. Stir in sprouts and coriander.

serves 4
per serving 1g fat; 806kJ (193 cal)

coconut rice

40g ghee
1 clove garlic, crushed
1 teaspoon cumin seeds
1 medium brown onion (150g), sliced
2 cups (400g) basmati rice
1½ cups (375ml) coconut milk
1⅓ cups (330ml) chicken stock

1 Heat ghee in large heavy-based saucepan, add garlic, seeds and onion; cook, stirring, until onion is soft.
2 Add rice; cook, stirring, 2 minutes. Stir in coconut milk and stock; simmer, covered, about 12 minutes or until rice is just tender.
3 Remove from heat; stand, covered, 10 minutes.

serves 4
per serving 30.3g fat; 2750kJ (658 cal)

carrot and cucumber salad

2 medium carrots (240g)
1 telegraph cucumber (400g), sliced thinly
3 cups (240g) bean sprouts, tips trimmed
1 tablespoon finely chopped fresh coriander
peanut dressing
⅓ cup (85g) smooth peanut butter
1 clove garlic, crushed
1 teaspoon sambal oelek
1 tablespoon soy sauce
½ cup (125ml) coconut milk
2 tablespoons hot water

1 Make peanut dressing.
2 Using vegetable peeler, shave long, thin strips from carrots.
Gently toss carrot with remaining ingredients in large bowl;
drizzle with peanut dressing.
peanut dressing Combine peanut butter, garlic, sambal,
sauce and coconut milk in small bowl. Just before serving,
stir in the water.

serves 4
per serving 17.5g fat; 968kJ (232 cal)
tip The salad and peanut dressing can be made 2 days ahead
and stored separately, covered, in the refrigerator.

deep-fried tofu with peanut sauce

600g firm tofu, drained
vegetable oil, for deep-frying
peanut sauce
1 fresh coriander root, chopped finely
1 fresh red thai chilli, seeded, chopped finely
2 cloves garlic, crushed
1 tablespoon sugar
2 tablespoons rice vinegar
⅓ cup (90g) crunchy peanut butter
½ cup (125ml) coconut milk

1 Wrap tofu in three sheets of absorbent paper,
weigh down with plate; stand 4 hours.
2 Meanwhile, make peanut sauce.
3 Cut tofu into 2cm cubes. Heat oil in large wok; deep-fry
tofu, in batches, until well browned, drain on absorbent paper.
Serve hot with warm peanut sauce; sprinkle with fresh
coriander and chilli, if desired.
peanut sauce Combine coriander root, chilli, garlic, sugar
and vinegar in small saucepan; stir over heat until sugar
dissolves. Stir in peanut butter and coconut milk, until just hot.

serves 6
per serving 25g fat; 1343kJ (321 cal)

potatoes and spinach

40g ghee
2 teaspoons grated fresh ginger
1 teaspoon ground turmeric
1 teaspoon garam masala
1 teaspoon chilli powder
4 medium potatoes (800g), unpeeled, chopped coarsely
1 cup (250ml) water
650g spinach

1 Heat ghee in heated large wok; cook ginger, turmeric, garam masala and chilli, stirring, until fragrant. Add potato; cook, stirring, 1 minute.
2 Add the water; simmer, covered, about 15 minutes or until potato is tender.
3 Stir in spinach; cook, covered, 2 minutes.

serves 4
per serving 10.8g fat; 1035kJ (248 cal)j

fried tofu and green vegetables

We used packaged fried tofu which you can buy from supermarkets. However, if you prefer to do it yourself, you can shallow-fry cubes of firm tofu in vegetable oil until browned lightly, then drain on absorbent paper.

1 tablespoon peanut oil
1 large brown onion (200g), sliced thickly
2 cloves garlic, crushed
1 tablespoon grated fresh ginger
2 red thai chillies, chopped finely
200g green beans
250g asparagus
500g baby bok choy, quartered
500g choy sum, chopped coarsely
1 tablespoon fish sauce
2 tablespoons sweet chilli sauce
2 tablespoons brown sugar
¼ cup (60ml) lime juice
300g fried tofu
¼ cup loosely packed, coarsely chopped fresh coriander
¼ cup loosely packed, coarsely chopped fresh mint

1 Heat oil in wok; stir-fry onion, garlic, ginger and chilli until onion just softens.
2 Add beans and asparagus; stir-fry until tender. Add bok choy, choy sum, sauces, sugar and juice; stir-fry until bok choy just wilts. Add tofu and herbs; stir-fry until hot.

serves 4
per serving 9.9g fat; 850kJ (203 cal)
tip Most vegetables can be stir-fried successfully, but ensure they are as dry as possible before cooking to prevent them becoming soggy.

tamarind sambal

1 tablespoon tamarind concentrate
2 tablespoons water
1 teaspoon ground cumin
½ teaspoon chilli powder
½ teaspoon ground fennel
1½ tablespoons palm sugar
2 teaspoons grated fresh ginger
1 tablespoon lemon juice

1 Combine tamarind and the water in small bowl; stir until dissolved.
2 Stir cumin, chilli and fennel into tamarind mixture.
3 Stir in palm sugar, ginger and juice, stir until sugar is dissolved.

makes ½ cup (125g)
per ½ cup 1g fat; 756kJ (181 cal)
tip The sambal can be made a day ahead; store, covered, in the refrigerator.

fresh coriander and coconut chutney

⅓ cup (80ml) boiling water
⅓ cup (25g) shredded coconut
2 cups loosely packed fresh coriander leaves
4 cloves garlic, chopped
1 small brown onion (80g), chopped
1½ teaspoons garam masala
¼ cup (60ml) lemon juice
2 tablespoons lime juice
1 small fresh red thai chilli, chopped

1 Pour the water over coconut in small bowl, cover; stand about 5 minutes or until liquid is absorbed.
2 Blend or process coconut mixture, coriander, garlic, onion, garam masala and juices until well combined. Return mixture to bowl; stir in chilli.

makes about 1½ cups (400g)
per 100g 4.8g fat; 269kJ (64 cal)
tip The chutney can be made a day ahead; store, covered, in the refrigerator.

index

conversion chart

MEASURES

One Australian metric measuring cup holds approximately 250ml, one Australian metric tablespoon holds 20ml, one Australian metric teaspoon holds 5ml.

The difference between one country's measuring cups and another's is within a two- or three-teaspoon variance, and will not affect your cooking results. North America, New Zealand and the United Kingdom use a 15ml tablespoon.

All cup and spoon measurements are level. The most accurate way of measuring dry ingredients is to weigh them. When measuring liquids, use a clear glass or plastic jug with the metric markings.

We use large eggs with an average weight of 60g.

DRY MEASURES

METRIC	IMPERIAL
15g	½oz
30g	1oz
60g	2oz
90g	3oz
125g	4oz (¼lb)
155g	5oz
185g	6oz
220g	7oz
250g	8oz (½lb)
280g	9oz
315g	10oz
345g	11oz
375g	12oz (¾lb)
410g	13oz
440g	14oz
470g	15oz
500g	16oz (1lb)
750g	24oz (1½lb)
1kg	32oz (2lb)

LIQUID MEASURES

METRIC	IMPERIAL
30ml	1 fluid oz
60ml	2 fluid oz
100ml	3 fluid oz
125ml	4 fluid oz
150ml	5 fluid oz (¼ pint/1 gill)
190ml	6 fluid oz
250ml	8 fluid oz
300ml	10 fluid oz (½ pint)
500ml	16 fluid oz
600ml	20 fluid oz (1 pint)
1000ml (1 litre)	1¾ pints

LENGTH MEASURES

METRIC	IMPERIAL
3mm	⅛in
6mm	¼in
1cm	½in
2cm	¾in
2.5cm	1in
5cm	2in
6cm	2½in
8cm	3in
10cm	4in
13cm	5in
15cm	6in
18cm	7in
20cm	8in
23cm	9in
25cm	10in
28cm	11in
30cm	12in (1ft)

OVEN TEMPERATURES

These oven temperatures are only a guide for conventional ovens.
For fan-forced ovens, check the manufacturer's manual.

	°C (CELSIUS)	°F (FAHRENHEIT)	GAS MARK
Very slow	120	250	½
Slow	150	275 – 300	1 – 2
Moderately slow	170	325	3
Moderate	180	350 – 375	4 – 5
Moderately hot	200	400	6
Hot	220	425 – 450	7 – 8
Very hot	240	475	9

Are you missing some of the world's favourite cookbooks?

The Australian Women's Weekly cookbooks are available from bookshops, cookshops, supermarkets and other stores all over the world. You can also buy direct from the publisher, using the order form below.

MINI SERIES £2.50 190x138MM 64 PAGES

TITLE	QTY	TITLE	QTY	TITLE	QTY
4 Fast Ingredients		Crumbles & Bakes		Noodles	
15-minute Feasts		Curries		Outdoor Eating	
30-minute Meals		Drinks		Party Food	
50 Fast Chicken Fillets		Fast Fish		Pasta	
After-work Stir-fries		Fast Food for Friends		Pickles and Chutneys	
Barbecue		Fast Soup		Potatoes	
Barbecue Chicken		Finger Food		Risotto	
Barbecued Seafood		Gluten-free Cooking		Roast	
Biscuits, Brownies & Biscotti		Healthy Everyday Food 4 Kids		Salads	
Bites		Ice-creams & Sorbets		Simple Slices	
Bowl Food		Indian Cooking		Simply Seafood	
Burgers, Rösti & Fritters		Indonesian Favourites		Skinny Food	
Cafe Cakes		Italian		Stir-fries	
Cafe Food		Italian Favourites		Summer Salads	
Casseroles		Jams & Jellies		Tapas, Antipasto & Mezze	
Char-grills & Barbecues		Kids Party Food		Thai Cooking	
Cheesecakes, Pavlovas & Trifles		Last-minute Meals		Thai Favourites	
Chinese Favourites		Lebanese Cooking		Vegetarian	
Chocolate Cakes		Malaysian Favourites		Vegetarian Stir-fries	
Christmas Cakes & Puddings		Mince		Vegie Main Meals	
Cocktails		Muffins		Wok	
				TOTAL COST	£

Photocopy and complete coupon below

Name _____

Address _____

_____ Postcode _____

Country _____ Phone (business hours) _____

Email*(optional) _____

By including your email address, you consent to receipt of any email regarding this magazine, and other emails which inform you of ACP's other publications, products, services and events, and to promote third party goods and services you may be interested in.

I enclose my cheque/money order for £ _____

or please charge £ _____ to my:

☐ Bankcard ☐ Mastercard ☐ Visa ☐ American Express ☐ Diners Club

Card number | | | | | | | | | | | | | | | | |

Cardholder's signature _____ Expiry date ____ / ____

To order: Mail or fax – photocopy or complete the order form above, and send your credit card details or cheque payable to: Australian Consolidated Press (UK), Moulton Park Business Centre, Red House Road, Moulton Park, Northampton NN3 6AQ, phone (+44) (01) 604 497531, fax (+44) (01) 604 497533, email books@acpmedia.co.uk. Or order online at www.acpuk.com
Non-UK residents: We accept the credit cards listed on the coupon, or cheques, drafts or International Money Orders payable in sterling and drawn on a UK bank. Credit card charges are at the exchange rate current at the time of payment.
Postage and packing UK: Add £1.00 per order plus 25p per book.
Postage and packing overseas: Add £2.00 per order plus 50p per book.
Offer ends 30.06.2006